Fundamentals of Inorganic Chemistry

A Programmed Introduction

D1546163

HEYDEN PROGRAMMED TEXTS

Infrared Spectroscopy

A Programmed Introduction to Infrared Spectroscopy
B.W. Cook and K. Jones

Requiring no prior knowledge of the subject, this book teaches the principles and practice of infrared spectroscopy, for routine analytical work in the modern laboratory, using programmed instruction methods.

The Interpretation of Infrared Spectra
A Programmed Introduction
R.R. Hill and D.A.E. Rendell

This student-active book builds into the learning process the experience needed to interpret infrared spectra. Basic principles and the use of empirical data are emphasised, and there is a comprehensive section on experimental technique. Extensive correlation charts are included, and altogether this is also a useful handbook when using infrared analysis in the laboratory.

Nuclear Magnetic Resonance Spectroscopy

The Interpretation of Proton Magnetic Resonance Spectra
A Programmed Introduction
E.J. Haws, R.R. Hill and D.J. Mowthorpe

Six graduated stages lead the beginner to a full appreciation of the assignment of structure to particular features of proton magnetic resonance spectra.

Gas-Liquid Chromatography

A Programmed Introduction to Gas-Liquid Chromatography
J.B. Pattison   2nd Edition

The book teaches gas-liquid chromatography in a logical progression, and is also designed to be used as a reference work and fault finder in everyday problem solving.

HEYDEN LEARNING CARDS

Organic Chemistry Revision Cards

Chemsyn
G. Eglinton and J.R. Maxwell

50 playing-type cards show the important reactions and preparations of 50 compounds drawn from a range of chemical classes, both aliphatic and aromatic. They are excellent for revision and as a teaching aid.

A Games Approach to the Chemical Elements

Element Cards
J.I. Lipson

105 playing-type cards, giving physical and chemical properties of the 105 elements known to date. Property relationships are emphasised, and the set provides the portable material for stimulating interest, involvement and motivation in learning about the elements.

Fundamentals of Inorganic Chemistry

A Programmed Introduction

Edited by

B. J. Aylett

Westfield College, University of London

D. E. Billing

Council for National Academic Awards, London

LONDON   NEW YORK   RHEINE

Heyden & Son Ltd., Spectrum House, Alderton Crescent, London NW4 3X?

Heyden & Son Inc., 225 Park Avenue, New York, N.Y. 10017, U.S.A.

Heyden & Son GmbH, 4440 Rheine/Westf., Münsterstrasse 22, Germany.

© Heyden & Son Ltd., 1975

All Rights Reserved. No part of this publication may be reproduced, stored in a retrieval system, or transmitted, in any form or by any means electronic, mechanical, photocopying, recording or otherwise, without the prior permission of Heyden & Son Ltd.

ISBN 0 85501 095 9

Printed by Ceuterick NV, Leuven, Belgium.

546.077
A978f

Contents

Foreword

Programmed instruction is increasingly becoming recognised as an effective tool of modern educational technology. A properly designed sequence of frames enables students to learn concepts properly and at their own pace. This mode of self-instruction has been successful in a variety of situations in chemistry. I am glad that the authors of this text have written this elegant programmed introduction to the fundamentals of inorganic chemistry. It is heartening that the authors have related descriptive aspects of inorganic chemistry to fundamental principles and made the subject interesting. This is important since there is often the danger that inorganic chemistry becomes an ensemble of assorted facts. To my knowledge, this is one of the few programmed texts dealing with unified inorganic chemistry. I have no doubt that this book will be found useful by teachers and students alike.

Oxford, May 1975   C.N.R. RAO

Senior Professor of Chemistry,
Indian Institute of Technology,
Kanpur, India.
(Chairman, IUPAC Committee
in Teaching of Chemistry)

Preface

The contributors to this book have been meeting as a group since 1970, when some initial versions of these programmes were prepared. The group came together out of a need to produce materials which students could use to supplement or complement lecture courses in inorganic chemistry at the first-year university level. The task was felt to be so large as to demand a sharing of the work. This arrangement had important additional advantages: it enabled members to discuss ideas and common problems, it exposed draft programmes to intensive constructive criticism, and it provided access to a larger "pool" of students on which to test the materials.

Originally the group intended to produce programmes on descriptive inorganic chemistry. It became obvious, however, that the only way to treat this area was to relate as much of the content as possible to fundamental principles. At this stage, the group found a lack of learning materials which dealt with the fundamental principles at the right level, and the first task then became the rectification of this deficiency. From the beginning, this set of 7 programmes was seen as a linked and coherent package, and it therefore seemed sensible to publish them together. The tables and the third programme (*Electronic Screening and Effective Nuclear Charge*) were prepared to meet needs identified during the writing of the other programmes. The aim has been to provide treatment suitable for first-degree students and those taking professional or advanced technician courses: some of the material is also relevant to advanced school and further education syllabuses.

The individual programmes may also be used separately, since each is provided with a list of objectives, a test and a summary. Thus, Chapter 5, *Electronegativity*, depends on Chapter 1, *Electronic Configuration of Atoms; The Periodic Table*, and on Chapter 4, *Ionisation Energies and Electron Affinities*; students who wish to proceed directly to programme 5 should first see whether they can pass the tests set at the end of programmes 1 and 4. Similar procedures apply to the other programmes.

The format of printed linear programmes has been chosen due to its simplicity and convenience; students can take the material home, which is not generally true of videotape or tape/slide sequences. These programmes are also relatively inexpensive, so that libraries can easily purchase multiple copies and students can afford their own copies. Although many students will be able to learn from these programmes without having first attended any lectures on the topics (the book is in this sense self-contained), we cannot emphasise too strongly that the purpose of programmed learning is not to replace lectures, but to provide materials for those students who need extra help or who have missed lectures or who learn most readily from such materials. In short, these programmes are intended as a flexible addition to teaching arrangements which already exist.

The limited scope of these programmes needs to be acknowledged. Any good modern textbook of inorganic chemistry will show that here is a subject with important implications for areas as diverse as metallurgy, enzymatic processes, ceramic science, air and water pollution, and industrial catalysis. Inorganic chemists seek to rationalise their large subject in terms of certain conceptual principles; the programmes here are a kit of tools for building a better understanding of those principles. We plan to follow them with a set of programmes in which the principles are applied to the chemistry of representative elements.

Since the initial versions were prepared, several revisions of the programmes have been made, at all stages involving trials with large numbers of students in universities and polytechnics. At one stage, with the invaluable help of The Chemical Society, a total of 2386 copies of individual programmes (from 250 to 400 of each) were sent to 18 institutions, each with a questionnaire inviting general reactions and comments on the difficulty of particular frames. The responses were very favourable and the detailed comments gave authors much help in revising the programmes. At an earlier stage, a smaller sample of 55 students in one university were supervised during their studies of some of the programmes, and the following numerical data were collected.

	Programme				
	1	4	5	6	7
Mean time for completion (minutes)	60	82	75	65	75
Percentage of correct responses	95	84	81	90	85

The students found the programmes useful and commented favourably on the different styles. We have retained this variety of approach during the editing.

Comments on the book as a whole will be welcomed by the editors, and comments on individual programmes may be sent to their authors.

February 1975   B. J. AYLETT
                                                                                   D. E. BILLING

Instructions on Using the Programmes

Programmed learning takes the reader step by step through a sequence of **frames** in which the demand for a response ensures that he understands the concept before passing to the next frame. Thus, you cannot just read, you must read and think as you complete the programme. This is not a test, and there is no time limit; however, you should be able to get at least 80% of the answers correct.

The answers are written below each frame. Cover up the answer with a piece of paper and write your answer before exposing the correct one. Write your responses in a notebook or on sheets of paper, preserving the programme for repeated use. If your response is incorrect, re-read the frame and see how the correct answer has been obtained. Then continue in the same way through the other frames in the text.

The form of the questions is varied through the book. In some cases direct questions are asked, in others blank spaces are left which complete sentences when filled, while in others alternative answers are suggested in the form: "A is *greater/smaller* than B" or "The resulting type of bond is termed *coordinate/metallic/van der Waals*".

Chapter 1

Electronic Configuration of Atoms
The Periodic Table

Dr. R. F. M. White

City of London Polytechnic, London EC3N 2EY

Introduction

An atom consists of a small positively charged nucleus surrounded by negatively charged electrons. In any neutral atom the number of electrons is such that the total negative charge on the electrons balances the positive charge on the nucleus. The chemical properties of an element depend on the number and arrangement (configuration) of the electrons in the atoms of the element. In this programme we will consider the way in which the electronic configurations of atoms of different elements can be built up using, in a qualitative way, the results of theoretical calculations. We will then see how the configurations relate to the positions of elements in the Periodic Classification, which was originally based on chemical properties.

Prior Knowledge

It is not possible to know both the exact position and the exact momentum of a microscopic particle such as an electron. The Schrödinger equation provides a description of the behaviour of such microscopic particles in terms of probabilities. The complete Schrödinger equation includes both space and time, but for our purpose it is sufficient to use the time-independent form of the equation; that is, we will deal with stationary states. Solutions of the Schrödinger equation (given the symbol Ψ) have significance for certain values (eigenvalues) of the energy E. In the solution of the Schrödinger equation for an electron in an atom, certain constants (quantum numbers) appear, and for the solutions to have physical significance the quantum numbers can have only certain allowed values. The quantum numbers are: n, the principal quantum number; l, the azimuthal or orbital quantum number; and m, the magnetic quantum number. We can specify a solution more closely by writing the values of n, l and m as subscripts to the symbol Ψ_{nlm}. A solution to the Schrödinger equation for an electron in an atom is called an orbital (or an atomic orbital if it is necessary to draw attention to the fact that it is a solution for the case of an atom), and if an orbital Ψ_{nlm} describes the behaviour of a particular electron, the electron is said to occupy that orbital. To complete the description of an electron a fourth quantum number, the spin quantum number m_s, has to be introduced.

Objectives

When you have completed this programme you should be able to:

1. List the three quantum numbers which describe an atomic orbital and give the relationship between these numbers.

2. Give the possible values of the spin quantum number for a single electron.

3. State the Pauli Exclusion Principle and interpret this in terms of the number of electrons which one orbital may contain.

4. Recognise and use the symbols for atomic orbitals.

5. List the usual order of filling of atomic orbitals by electrons.

6. Write down the electronic configuration of an element, given its atomic number.

7. State and apply Hund's rule to the electronic configuration of atoms.

8. Recognise and use a notation for the direction of spin of paired and unpaired electrons.

9. State the type of element, given its electronic configuration.

10. State the characteristic electronic configuration of each group of elements.

Programme Test

Before starting the programme itself, try the following test. Answers and scores are on p. 90. If you score greater than 16 you do not need to study the programme.

1. If the quantum number $n = 3$, what values can the quantum number l take? Give the allowed values of the quantum number m for each value of l.

2. What is the Pauli Exclusion Principle?

3. How many electrons may an orbital contain?

4. What does the symbol 3d mean when used to describe an atomic orbital?

5. What is the electronic configuration of a boron atom? (The atomic number of boron is 5.)

6. What feature of its electronic configuration characterises a transition element?

7. What feature of its electronic configuration characterises an inner transition element?

8. What is the valency shell configuration for each of the following elements?
   Ne (atomic number 10);   Ar (atomic number 18);   Kr (atomic number 36);
   Xe (atomic number 54);   Rn (atomic number 86).

9. What feature in their electronic configuration do the elements Na, K and Rb have in common?

F1.1 An atomic orbital is described by three quantum numbers, n, l and m. The first of these, n, can have integral values 1, 2, 3, 4 . . . . , while for an orbital with a given value of n, l can have values 0, 1, 2 . . . . up to $(n-1)$.

What are the possible values of l for an orbital having (a) $n = 1$; (b) $n = 2$?

- -

A1.1 (a) $l = 0$; (b) $l = 0$ or $l = 1$.

F1.2 What can you say about the value of n for an orbital which has $l = 3$?

- -

A1.2 n is an integer equal to or greater than 4.

F1.3 For a given value of l, m can have the integral values: l, $(l-1)$, $(l-2)$, . . . 0, -1, -2, . . . $-(l-1)$, $-(l)$. So for an orbital in which $l = 2$, m may be $+2$, $+1$, 0, -1, -2. What are the possible values of m for the orbital having $l = 4$? Write down the possible values of l and m for $n = 2$.

- -

A1.3 $l = 4$, m may be $+4$, $+3$, $+2$, $+1$, 0, -1, -2, -3, -4.
With $n = 2$, l may be 1 or 0.
When $n = 2$ and $l = 1$, m may be $+1$, 0, -1.
When $n = 2$ and $l = 0$, $m = 0$.

F1.4 A fourth quantum number m_s (the spin quantum number) can have the values $+\frac{1}{2}$ or $-\frac{1}{2}$. The value of m_s is not controlled by the values of the other quantum numbers.

What values of m_s are possible for the orbitals in which $n = 2$, $l = 1$ and $m = +1$?

- -

A1.4 $m_s = +\frac{1}{2}$ or $-\frac{1}{2}$.

F1.5 The Pauli Exclusion Principle states that in an atom no two electrons can have the same set of values for all four quantum numbers. For example, if in an atom one electron occupies the orbital for which $n = 1$, $l = 0$, $m = 0$, and has $m_s = +\frac{1}{2}$, no other electron will be able to occupy the same orbital and have the same value of m_s. However, a second electron would be able to occupy the same orbital if it had $m_s =$ _____ .

- -

A1.5 $-\frac{1}{2}$.

F1.6 We see that it is possible for two electrons to occupy the same orbital, i.e to have the same values of n, l and m, provided they have different values of m_s. Two electrons occupying the same orbital are said to have their spin paired.

In everyday language we can talk of an orbital being empty or occupied. As there are only two allowed values for m_s a particular orbital can contain a maximum of two electrons. An occupied orbital can contain either _____ or _____ electrons.

- -

A1.6 One, two.

F1.7 In the absence of a magnetic or an electric field, the energy of an electron in an orbital depends on the values of the quantum numbers n and l.

For a particular atom, two or more different orbitals may have the same value for their eigen energies, and such orbitals are said to be degenerate.

What orbitals in free space, i.e. in the absence of magnetic and electric fields, will be degenerate with the orbital having $n = 2$, $l = 1$ and $m = +1$?

A1.7 The orbitals with $n = 2$, $l = 1$, $m = 0$, and $n = 2$, $l = 1$, $m = -1$.

F1.8 It is useful to devise a symbol to distinguish different orbitals, and as the energies of orbitals, which depend on the quantum numbers _____ and _____, are of great importance we use the values of these quantum numbers as the basis for the symbols.

A1.8 n and l.

F1.9 The symbols used to designate orbitals consist of two parts; the first is a number which is equal to the value of n for the orbital. The second part of the symbol is a letter indicating the value of l for the orbital.

Thus: when $l = 0$ the letter used is s

$l = 1$	p
$l = 2$	d
$l = 3$	f
$l = 4$	g

These letters are used as a result of the terminology developed in early work on the spectra of atoms which has given much information about electronic configurations. For example, we would use the symbol 2p for the orbital having $n = 2$ and $l = 1$.

Write down the symbols for the following orbitals: (a) $n = 1$, $l = 0$; (b) $n = 2$, $l = 0$; (c) $n = 3$, $l = 2$.

A1.9 (a) 1s; (b) 2s; (c) 3d.

F1.10 It is useful to use numbers for n and letters for l so that one can talk about particular types of orbitals without constantly using phrases such as "orbitals having l equal to 0"; here one would simply refer to "s orbitals". As a letter has been used we are able to distinguish that the value of l is being given.

What factor is common to all p orbitals?

A1.10 All p orbitals have $l = 1$.

F1.11 We next have to consider the energies of an electron in different orbitals. A useful mnemonic device for remembering the order of orbital energies is as follows:

Write out the symbols for orbitals in columns, the first column being used for s orbitals, the second for p, the third for d and so on, putting the orbital with lowest value of n at the bottom of the column. Then draw a series of parallel diagonal lines as shown below; the order of orbital energies is now the order in which the symbols are struck by the diagonal lines.

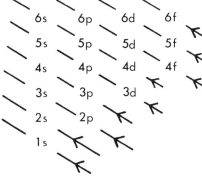

The order of increasing energy of the orbitals is 1s, 2s, 2p, 3s, 3p, 4s, 3d, 4p, 5s . . . . We will see later that there are one or two exceptions to the order predicted by this mnemonic, but these discrepancies are not numerous.

Is the 5d orbital of higher or lower energy than the 6s orbital?

_ _

       A1.11 Higher.

F1.12 When we work out the electronic configuration for an atom of atomic number Z, we imagine that we can start with only the nucleus and then consider adding Z electrons one at a time, each electron occupying the orbital of lowest energy that is available. Availability of orbitals is determined by the Pauli Exclusion Principle.

What is the Pauli Exclusion Principle?

_ _

       A1.12 The Pauli Exclusion Principle states that in an atom no two electrons can have the same set of values for all four quantum numbers (see **F1.5**).

F1.13 In writing down electronic configurations it is sometimes convenient to represent each orbital by a box:

☐

Each orbital can contain _____ electrons, provided that _____

_ _

       A1.13 Two; m_s is different for the two electrons, i.e. the spins are opposed.

F1.14 Each box can contain up to two electrons. We can represent the value of m_s by an arrow. The arrow pointing in one direction represents $m_s = +\frac{1}{2}$, while pointing in the opposite direction it represents $m_s = -\frac{1}{2}$. An orbital containing one electron could be drawn as:

$$\boxed{\uparrow}$$

How would you represent an orbital containing two electrons with opposed spins?

- -

     A1.14

$$\boxed{\uparrow\downarrow}$$

F1.15 In order of increasing energies, orbitals could be represented as follows:

The p orbitals appear as three boxes because when $l = 1$, m can be $+1$, 0 or -1. How many boxes will there be for d orbitals? Why?

- -

     A1.15 Five. m can be $+2, +1, 0, -1, -2$.

F1.16 Let us consider a few configurations.

Hydrogen ($Z = 1$). The single electron will occupy the 1s orbital and this can be represented as:

$$1s \quad \boxed{\uparrow}$$

This could also be written as $1s^1$, the superscript indicating that there is one electron in the 1s orbital.

Helium ($Z = 2$). The first electron will occupy the 1s orbital with, say, $m_s = +\frac{1}{2}$. The second electron will occupy the same orbital with $m_s = -\frac{1}{2}$. This can be represented as:

$$\text{He} \quad 1s \quad \boxed{\uparrow\downarrow} \quad \text{or} \quad 1s^2$$

Lithium ($Z = 3$). The first electron will occupy the 1s orbital with, say, $m_s = +\frac{1}{2}$, the second electron will occupy the same orbital with $m_s = -\frac{1}{2}$, but the third electron cannot occupy the 1s orbital. Why not?

- -

--- ---

A1.16 Because this would violate the Pauli Exclusion Principle. An orbital can contain a maximum of two electrons.

F1.17 The orbital of lowest energy available for the third electron of the lithium configuration is the ＿＿＿ orbital.

--- ---

A1.17 2s.

F1.18 The configuration for lithium can therefore be represented as:

2s　$\boxed{\uparrow}$

1s　$\boxed{\uparrow\downarrow}$

or $1s^2 2s^1$　or [He] $2s^1$.

For beryllium ($Z = 4$), the first electron will occupy the 1s orbital with, say, $m_s = +\frac{1}{2}$, the second electron will occupy the 1s orbital with $m_s = -\frac{1}{2}$, the third electron cannot occupy the 1s orbital and the orbital of lowest energy available is the 2s orbital—but this is the procedure we have been through before. Where?

--- ---

A1.18 For the three electrons in lithium.

F1.19 The first three electrons added in building up the beryllium configuration occupy orbitals in the same way as the three electrons of the lithium configuration. We could therefore start building up the beryllium configuration by saying that the first three electrons will have the configuration $1s^1 2s^1$ (as for lithium) and that all we have to do is to consider the fourth electron. This will occupy the 2s orbital giving the configuration

Be　2s　$\boxed{\uparrow\downarrow}$

1s　$\boxed{\uparrow\downarrow}$

or $1s^2 2s^2$　or [He] $2s^2$.

If we know the electronic configuration for the element of atomic number $Z = x$, then for the element with $Z = (x + 1)$ the first x electrons will adopt the same configuration as that of the element with $Z = x$.

What can be said about the configuration of the first four electrons involved in building up the boron atom?

--- ---

A1.19 They have the same configuration as the beryllium atom: $1s^2 2s^2$.

F1.20 The fifth electron of the boron configuration will occupy the ＿＿＿ orbital, giving the configuration ＿＿＿.

--- ---

A1.20 2p; $1s^2 2s^2 2p^1$.

F1.21 A problem arises with carbon ($Z = 6$), the element following boron. The first five electrons for the carbon configuration will adopt the ____ configuration.

A1.21 Boron.

F1.22 The boron configuration can be written in a box diagram as:

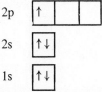

and for the sixth electron in the carbon configuration there are vacancies in the three 2p orbitals. We have to consider if one of the possible arrangements is of lower energy than the others. Two electrons will *attract/repel* one another and the interaction between two electrons will be least when the two electrons are *close/far apart*.

A1.22 Repel; far apart.

F1.23 Hund's rule tells us that when two electrons occupy a number of orbitals of equal energy, then the arrangement of electrons giving the lowest energy is that in which the electrons occupy different orbitals, i.e. occupy different regions of space, and have their spins parallel.

Which of the following possible configurations for carbon will be of lowest energy?

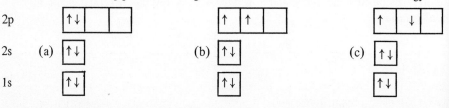

A1.23 (b).

F1.24 For a particular atom, the arrangement of electrons having lowest energy is called the ground state for that atom.

Write down, in the form of a box diagram, the ground state for the nitrogen atom ($Z = 7$ for nitrogen), remembering to label the boxes with the symbols 1s, 2s, etc.

A1.24

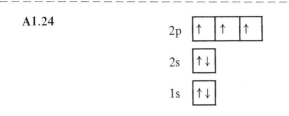

F1.25 For oxygen ($Z = 8$) the first seven electrons adopt the nitrogen configuration. Now, however, there is no vacant 2p orbital for the eighth electron to occupy, so this electron will occupy one of the half filled 2p orbitals.

Show the oxygen configuration as a box diagram.

A1.25

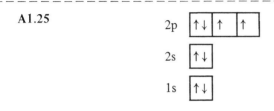

F1.26 Following on, draw box diagrams showing the configurations for the elements fluorine and neon.

A1.26

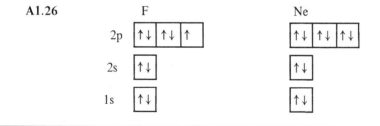

F1.27 After neon, for which the 2s and 2p orbitals are filled, electrons start to occupy the 3s and then the 3p orbitals. This process is completed with the element argon ($Z = 18$), after which the 4s orbital is occupied, potassium ($Z = 19$) having the configuration [Ar] 4s^1, and the following element calcium, [Ar] 4s^2. For the subsequent element, scandium, the orbital of lowest energy available after the calcium configuration is the ____ orbital. Therefore scandium has the configuration ____ .

A1.27 3d; [Ar] 3d^1 4s^2.

F1.28 With successive elements after scandium, the 3d orbitals are filled as follows (neglecting the electrons of the argon configuration).

Sc	Ti	V	Cr	Mn
$3d^1 4s^2$	$3d^2 4s^2$	$3d^3 4s^2$	$3d^5 4s^1$	$3d^5 4s^2$
Fe	Co	Ni	Cu	Zn
$3d^6 4s^2$	$3d^7 4s^2$	$3d^8 4s^2$	$3d^{10} 4s^1$	$3d^{10} 4s^2$

Elements in which electrons occupy an orbital of quantum number $n = x$ (here $x = 4$) and the orbitals with $n = (x - 1)$ [here $(x - 1) = 3$] are being filled, are called transition elements.

Where are there discontinuities in the process of building up the configurations of the transition elements in the series Sc to Zn?

A1.28 Discontinuities occur with the elements Cr and Cu.

F1.29 After zinc, the elements gallium to krypton have configurations in which the 4p orbitals are filled. These elements are followed by rubidium ($[Kr] 5s^1$) and strontium ($[Kr] 5s^2$). For the next element, yttrium ($Z = 39$), the first 38 electrons adopt the strontium configuration.

What is the orbital of lowest energy available for the final electron of the yttrium configuration?

A1.29 4d.

F1.30 In passing from yttrium to cadmium the d orbitals are being filled, so these elements form a second series of _____ elements.

A1.30 Transition. Again there are irregularities in the filling of the 4d orbitals. Check in the tables at the end of the book (p. 88) to find the configurations for this second transition series.

F1.31 After cadmium the 5p orbitals are being filled. This process ends with the element xenon which has the configuration $[Kr] 4d^{10} 5s^2 5p^6$. For the next element caesium ($Z = 55$) the configuration is ____, and for barium ($Z = 56$) the configuration is ____.

A1.31 Caesium, $[Xe] 6s^1$; Barium, $[Xe] 6s^2$.

F1.32 For lanthanum ($Z = 57$), we find that the mnemonic given in **F1.11** is not correct, and the ground state for lanthanum is $[Xe] 5d^1 6s^2$. However, for the next element, cerium, the configuration is $[Xe] 4f^2 6s^2$ which is in keeping with the scheme in **F1.11**. In the elements following on after cerium the 4f orbitals are being filled (see the table, p. 88, for details).

We now have a series of elements in which electrons occupy the orbital $n = x$ (here $x = 6$) while the orbitals with $n = (x - 2)$ [here $(x - 2) = 4$] are being filled. Elements showing this feature in their configurations are called inner transition elements. There are 14 inner transition elements at this stage because _____.

- -

A1.32 There are seven 4f orbitals that can contain a total of fourteen electrons.

F1.33 Lutetium has the configuration $[Xe]4f^{14}5d^{1}6s^{2}$. With the next element, hafnium, filling of the 5d orbitals continues, so that with hafnium and subsequent elements we have a further series of _____ elements.

- -

A1.33 Transition.

F1.34 After filling of the 5d orbitals the 6p orbitals are occupied, this process being completed at radon which has the configuration _____.

- -

A1.34 $[Xe]4f^{14}5d^{10}6s^{2}6p^{6}$.

F1.35 You will find that you have now met the principles involved in building up electronic configurations. You should now consult the table (p. 88) to find out the configurations of the elements after radon.

F1.36 We have mentioned two special types of configuration, those found for the transition elements and those for the inner transition elements. All the remaining ground state configurations (which have d, f, etc. orbitals either completely filled or completely empty) can be divided into two classes.

The first class consists of those elements having configurations in which, for any value of n, the s and p orbitals are either completely filled or completely empty. The first element in this class is helium ($1s^{2}$) and other elements of this type are neon, argon, krypton, xenon and radon, all of which have the valence shell configuration _____.

These elements are known as the noble gases, and they have similar chemical properties.

- -

A1.36 All have the valence shell configuration $s^{2}p^{6}$.

F1.37 The second class consists of the elements in which s and p orbitals of the valency shell are incompletely filled; these elements are classified as typical or main group elements.

Classify the following configurations:
- (a) $1s^{2}2s^{2}2p^{6}3s^{2}3p^{6}$;
- (b) $1s^{2}2s^{2}2p^{6}3s^{2}3p^{6}4s^{2}$;
- (c) $1s^{2}2s^{2}2p^{6}3s^{2}3p^{6}3d^{2}4s^{2}$.

- -

- -

A1.37 (a) Noble gas; (b) main group; (c) transition element.

F1.38 If we now try to start arranging elements on the basis of electronic configurations we start building up the following sort of pattern.

s^1	s^2		s^2p^1	s^2p^2	s^2p^3	s^2p^4	s^2p^5	s^2p^6
Li	Be		B	C	N	O	F	Ne
Na	Mg		Al	Si	P	S	Cl	Ar
K	Ca	TRANSITION ELEMENTS d orbitals being filled	Ga	Ge	As	Se	Br	Kr

It will be seen that this pattern, based on electronic configuration, leads to grouping of elements in much the same way as in the older periodic table based on the properties of the elements. In fact, a knowledge of the electronic configurations of the elements provides a firm basis for building up the periodic classification of the elements.

Now repeat the programme test on p. 2, and mark it as before. If you score greater than 16 you have successfully completed this programme.

Summary

1. An atomic orbital is described by three quantum numbers, n, l and m, which can have the following values.

    $n = 1, 2, 3, 4 \ldots \ldots$
    $l = 0, 1, 2, 3 \ldots \ldots (n-1)$
    $m = -l, -(l-1), -(l-2) \ldots \ldots -2, -1, 0, 1, 2 \ldots \ldots (l-2), (l-1), l$

2. Atomic orbitals are described by symbols such as 2p, where the number is the principal quantum number (n) and the letter represents the orbital quantum number (l).

3. Apart from s orbitals, all orbitals are degenerate, to a degree given by the number of possible values of the magnetic quantum number (m). The number of orbitals of the same energy is $(2l + 1)$.

4. The fourth quantum number m_s refers to the electron spin and can take only the values $+\frac{1}{2}$ or $-\frac{1}{2}$ (represented by $\boxed{\uparrow}$ and $\boxed{\downarrow}$) for a single electron.

5. Since the Pauli Exclusion Principle states that in an atom no two electrons can have the same set of values for all four quantum numbers it follows that each orbital Ψ_{nlm} can hold a maximum of two electrons.

6. As we proceed from element to element, in order of increasing atomic numbers, electrons enter the available atomic orbitals of lowest energy. The order of filling is generally 1s, 2s, 2p, 3s, 3p, 4s, 3d, 4p, 5s, ... Each of these levels can contain $2(2l + 1)$ electrons.

7. Electronic configurations are represented by the symbols for the atomic orbitals, with superscripts indicating the number of electrons. Thus carbon is represented by $1s^2 2s^2 2p^2$. Sometimes, instead of this, the next lowest noble gas "core" is used to simplify the notation; thus $[Ar] 3d^3 4s^2$ is used to represent vanadium.

8. Hund's rule tells us that when two electrons occupy a number of orbitals of equal energy, then the arrangement of electrons with lowest energy is that in which the electrons occupy different orbitals with parallel spins.

9. The periodic table may be seen as being divided into the s-block elements (outer configuration s^1 or s^2), the p-block elements (p^1 to p^6), the transition elements (d^1 to d^{10}) and the inner transition elements (f^1 to f^{14}). The s and p blocks, taken together, are referred to as the "main group" elements.

Chapter 2

Atomic Size and Coordination Number

Dr. D. R. Pollard

City of London Polytechnic, London EC3N 2EY.

Introduction

The previous programme has treated the arrangements of atoms into groups and periods in the periodic table, according to the number of electrons surrounding the nucleus. In this programme we consider how the size of atoms and ions varies with electronic structure, and how molecular structure depends on these sizes. The concept of coordination number is introduced and related to atomic and ionic radii.

Prior Knowledge

You should be conversant with the contents of Chapter 1, and a test is given in the previous programme so that you can check this.

Objectives

When you have completed this programme you should be able to:

1. Describe roughly the way in which atomic size depends on the principal quantum number of the valence electrons.

2. State the limitations applying to the concept of a definite atomic radius.

3. Describe the relationships between atomic radius, Bohr radius, and the radial distribution function.

4. Suggest some methods for measuring bond lengths.

5. Calculate atomic (covalent/metallic) and ionic radii from bond length data.

6. State the significance of knowing the compound which is the source of radius data, and select the correct radius to use in calculations.

7. Describe the relationships between atomic size and the ionisation energy and electron affinity.

8. State a general rule for determining whether a given cation is larger or smaller than a given anion, and list the exceptions to this rule.

9. Describe the trend of ionic and atomic radii in a group and a period of the periodic table, and also the dependence of ionic radius upon ionic charge.

10. Define the concept of "coordination number", list its common values and state the corresponding stereochemical arrangements.

11. Define the term "radius ratio" and calculate its critical values for the important stereochemistries.

12. Describe the effects on radii of the d-block contraction and the lanthanide contraction, giving examples.

13. Define the van der Waals radius of an atom and relate its value to the covalent radius.

Programme Test

Before starting the programme itself, try the following test. Answers and scores are on p. 90. If you score greater than 25 you do not need to study the programme.

1. Which is the larger atom of those which have the following electronic configurations: $2s^2 2p^1$ or $3s^2 3p^1$?

2. How far may atomic radius be given a meaning in relation to the radial probability distribution?

3. Given the following bond lengths, deduce the values of the covalent radii of the elements involved: $C-H$, $1.1Å$; $H-I$, $1.6Å$; $C-I$, $2.1Å$.

4. List two methods of determining bond lengths and hence atomic and ionic radii.

5. Describe the factors which may cause the covalent or ionic radii to vary, depending on the compounds in which they were measured.

6. How do ionisation energy and electron affinity depend on atomic size?

7. Which is the larger species in each of the following cases?
    (a) Cl^- or Cl (b) Ca^{2+} or Ca (c) Fe^{2+} or Fe^{3+} (d) N or As
    (e) Al or S (f) Ti^{2+} or Cu^{2+} (g) Zr or Hf (h) Ba^{2+} or Cl^-
    (i) Cs^+ or F^- (j) Na^+ or Al^{3+}

8. What is meant by "coordination number"?

9. Give the common values of the coordination number and names of the corresponding geometrical arrangement of atoms or ions.

10. In ionic crystals, is the structure usually determined by the packing of cations around an anion or by anions around a cation?

11. In rutile (TiO_2) the coordination numbers are 6 and 3. What is the minimum value of the radius ratio for which this type of structure is possible?

12. Consider what would be the lower limit of the radius ratio in a compound having the rare trigonal bipyramidal coordination.

13. Define the van der Waals radius of an atom.

F2.1 The distance of an electron from the nucleus is given by the **radial probability distribution**. The probability of finding the electron at a given distance from the nucleus is plotted against distance for the 1s, 2s, 2p, 3s, 3p and 3d orbitals of the hydrogen atom below. These distributions may be obtained from the application of **quantum mechanics** to the hydrogen atom.

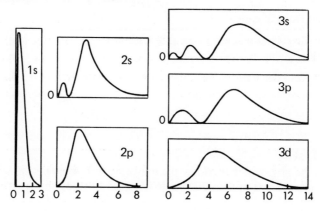

From these curves, the probability of finding the electron at the nucleus (origin) is always _____ .

      A2.1 Zero.

F2.2 Also the distribution varies according to the p_____q_____n_____ .

      A2.2 Principal quantum number.

F2.3 So that the larger the principal quantum number, the _____ the electron is *likely* to be from the nucleus, and the _____ the atom.

      A2.3 Further, larger.

F2.4 In addition, each curve reaches a m_____m.

      A2.4 Maximum.

F2.5 There is always a probability of finding an electron at a distance other than this maximum. For atoms with more than one electron, calculation of the radial probability distributions becomes very difficult, and the probable distance of an electron from the nucleus cannot be calculated with precision, though the general shape of the curves will be the same as for the hydrogen atom.

Note: The radial probability distribution must be considered with the angular distribution for a complete picture of finding an electron in any orbital.

F2.6 We may conclude that, though the radial probability distribution falls off *slowly/sharply* with increase in distance from the nucleus after the _____ has been passed, it is not possible to quote a _____ value for the radius of an atom, as there is a small but definite probability of the electron being found between _____ and _____ .

_ _

A2.6 Sharply, maximum, precise or definite, zero, infinity.

F2.7 Also the position of the maximum may not be predicted theoretically with any _____ . This maximum corresponds to the position of the Bohr electronic orbit.

_ _

A2.7 Accuracy.

F2.8 In the solid state, atoms approach each other closely, and take up a position such that the forces of bonding, i.e. *attraction/repulsion*, just balance the forces between the positively charged nuclei, i.e. _____ . Thus the atoms will take up an e_____m position.

_ _

A2.8 Attraction, repulsion, equilibrium.

F2.9 Realising its limitation, there is then some significance to the term **atomic radius**, and the distance between nuclear centres has a precise meaning in the solid state. Thus the atomic radius of a metal atom will be half the internuclear distance in the metal. If we could assign radii to all elements using this property of solids, then we could predict the _____ in compounds.

_ _

A2.9 Bond length or interatomic distance.

F2.10 Several physical techniques are available to determine the arrangement of atoms in space. The most important of these is _____ . Others are _____ and _____ .

_ _

A2.10 X-ray diffraction; spectra, magnetic measurements, dipole moments.

F2.11 Radii calculated from these physical measurements can only be used additively to predict other bond lengths if they have been determined by measurements on materials which have the same type of bonding. To illustrate these points let us consider the C–Cl bond in methyl chloride. X-ray diffraction evidence shows that the C–C distance in diamond is 1.54Å. This represents the distance between the centres of the two C nuclei, thus the atomic radius of C will be _____ Å.

_ _

A2.11 $\frac{1}{2} \times 1.54 = 0.77\text{Å}$.

F2.12 Similarly the Cl–Cl bond length in the Cl_2 molecule is 1.98Å. Thus the atomic radius is _____ Å.

A2.12 $\frac{1}{2} \times 1.98 = 0.99\text{Å}$.

F2.13 Therefore we would predict the C–Cl bond length in methyl chloride to be _____ Å.

A2.13 $0.99 + 0.77 = 1.76\text{Å}$.

F2.14 This compares with a measured value of 1.77Å. Thus the agreement between the calculated and observed values is _____ .

A2.14 Excellent.

F2.15 Diamond, chlorine and methyl chloride all contain _____ bonds only.

A2.15 Covalent.

F2.16 If we had used NaCl to derive the Cl atomic radius, a value of 1.81Å would have been found, giving a very poor agreement between observed and calculated bond lengths. The bonding in NaCl is _____ . We are therefore measuring the radius of Cl^- and not Cl. This is called the _____ **radius**.

A2.16 Ionic; **ionic**.

F2.17 Thus we have two series of radii for use in _____ and _____ compounds.

A2.17 Covalent, ionic.

F2.18 Instead of using the general term atomic radius, we will now specify either the **covalent radius** or the **ionic radius** according to the bonding involved.

Calculate the length of Si–H bond in SiH_4, given that the Si–Si bond length in elemental silicon is 2.34Å, and the H–H bond length in H_2 is 0.74Å. Thus the Si–H bond length is _____ Å.

The bonding in each of these compounds is _____ and therefore the agreement between the observed and calculated values should be *good/moderate/bad*.

- -

A2.18 1.54Å; covalent; moderate, there is an ionic contribution.

Thus we see a further limitation of the concept in that bonding is seldom purely covalent or ionic.

F2.19 The further an electron is from the nucleus, the less firmly it is held. Thus in the series (Li, Na, K, Rb, Cs), Cs has the most electrons and is the largest (ionic radius: Cs^+, 1.7Å; Li^+, 0.6Å), and therefore most easily forms a cation. (See Chapter 4, *Ionisation Energies and Electron Affinities*.)

Similarly in the series Mg, Ca, Sr, Ba; _____ is the largest and will ionise most easily.

- -

A2.19 Ba; refer to the table of data on pp. 85–87.

F2.20 In the case of the formation of anions, the smaller the anion the more easily can the nuclear charge hold the extra electrons. (See Chapter 4, *Ionisation Energies and Electron Affinities*.) Thus elements forming anions are small; among the most common are _____.

- -

A2.20 H^-, the halides, O^{2-}, S^{2-}, etc.; see the table of data on pp. 85–87.

F2.21 In a pure metal the covalent radius will be _____.

- -

A2.21 Half the interatomic distance.

F2.22 For non-metals, covalent radii are determined from compounds having a _____ bond, e.g. N–N from $H_2N–NH_2$.

- -

A2.22 Covalent.

F2.23 If we determine the value of the carbon covalent radius from ethylene we find a value of 0.66Å whereas calculation from ethane gives a value of 0.77Å. The ethane value is higher because _____.

- -

A2.23 In ethylene we have multiple bonds.

It is generally true that covalent radii will be incorrect if multiple bonds are present in the compounds on which measurements are made.

F2.24 To calculate ionic radii, ionic compounds must be used, but it is not obvious in what proportion the internuclear distance must be divided, e.g. for Cl^- in NaCl.

There have been several approaches to the problem, all of which have used an empirical method to produce tables of ionic radii. The values of Goldschmidt and Pauling which were produced independently are generally accepted. The Pauling values are based on a less empirical approach than the Goldschmidt values. Typical values are shown in the tables on pp. 82–85.

Several general deductions can be made from these tables:

   (i) Cations are normally *larger/smaller* than anions with four exceptions which are

      _____ .

     A2.24 Smaller; Rb^+, Cs^+, Fr^+ and Ra^{2+} are all larger than F^-.

F2.25 (ii) Within a vertical group the radius increases with an *increase/decrease* in atomic number.

     A2.25 Increase.

F2.26 (iii) Within a horizontal period, for isoelectronic ions the ionic radius *increases/ decreases* rapidly with increase in charge.

     A2.26 Decreases.

F2.27 (iv) Successive increases in valency of a cation will progressively _____ its radius.

     A2.27 Decrease.

F2.28 It is important to remember the limitations inherent in the concept of atomic radii given in the first few frames of this programme, and to limit its use accordingly. The same limitations apply to covalent and ionic radii.

Additionally, for ionic compounds it is found that the ionic radius varies according to the number of ions surrounding the ion in question. This number is called the

_____ .

     A2.28 Coordination number .

F2.29 The common coordination numbers are _____ , _____ , _____ and _____ .

     A2.29 3, 4, 6 and 8.

F2.30 The geometric arrangement of these ions about the central ion tends to be the most symmetric for each coordination number. Thus for coordination number 3 this would be _____ , for 4 _____ , for 6 _____ and for 8 _____ .

     A2.30 Trigonal, tetrahedral, octahedral, cubic. Note that other arrangements can be more stable in special cases, particularly with 8-coordination.

F2.31 The values of ionic radius given in the table on pp. 82–85 refer to 6-coordination. The interionic r_____f_____ experienced by a given ion will be different for other coordination numbers and will change its effective radius.

A2.31 Repulsive forces.

F2.32 As cations are generally *smaller/larger* than anions, the coordination number is usually determined in simple crystal structures by the number of anions it is possible to pack symmetrically round the cation. This can be expressed in terms of the **radius ratio**

$$\rho = \frac{r_{\text{cation}}}{r_{\text{anion}}}$$

As ρ increases, a point will be reached when for anion/cation contact to be maintained the coordination number must change. Values of these critical ρ can be used to predict crystal structure.

Complete the following table by simple trigonometry.

Coordination number of of cations	Symmetry of anions round cation	Critical values of ρ
2	linear	0.000 to 0.155
3	trigonal	0.155 to . . . . .
4	tetrahedral	. . . . . to . . . . .
6 (or 4)	octahedral	. . . . . to . . . . .
8	cubic	. . . . . to 1.000

A2.32 Smaller; 0.155 to 0.225; 0.225 to 0.414; 0.414 to 0.732; 0.732 to 1.000. Consider the effect of polarisation on this table when you have completed the programme on polarisability, Chapter 6.

F2.33 Using the values of ionic radii quoted in the tables, pp. 82–85, complete the following table.

	AgF	AgCl	AgBr	AgI
Calculated interatomic distance, Å	2.5	. . . .	. . . .	. . . .
Observed interatomic distance, Å	2.5	2.8	2.9	2.8
Percentage difference = $\dfrac{(\text{observed} - \text{calculated})}{(\text{observed})} \times 100$	0	. . . .	. . . .	. . . .

		AgCl	AgBr	AgI
A2.33 Calculated distance		3.0	3.2	3.4
Percentage difference		−7	−10	−21

F2.34 This increasing difference between the calculated and observed values is due to the _____ of the bonding, and illustrates a further general point requiring care in the use of ionic radii.

A2.34 Increasing covalent character.

F2.35 The trends in covalent radius follow the same pattern as those for ionic radius discussed in **F2.25** onwards. Thus they *increase/decrease* in a vertical group, and *increase/decrease* from left to right across a horizontal period.

A2.35 Increase, decrease.

F2.36 In addition, the horizontal decrease combined with the vertical increase leads to an interesting effect where d and f levels are being filled, i.e. in the 1st and 3rd long periods particularly. We illustrate this by comparing the sizes of Al and Ga. First recall their electronic configurations. Al has the configuration _____ and Ga _____.

A2.36 $[Ne] 3s^2 3p^1$; $[Ar] 4s^2 3d^{10} 4p^1$.

F2.37 $Ca (4s^2)$ has a larger covalent radius than $Mg (3s^2)$, and so $Ga (4s^2 4p^1)$ would be expected to be _____ than $Al (3s^2 3p^1)$, but due to the effect of the d electrons Ga is almost identical in radius to Al. This effect is called d-block contraction.

A2.37 Larger.

F2.38 In the f-block elements, the same effect is observed and is called f-block or lanthanide contraction. Thus Hf has a *larger/smaller* covalent radius than Zr. Here the effect is even more noticeable than in the d-block elements.

A2.38 Smaller.

F2.39 Complete the following from the tables provided at the end of the book, pp. 82–85.

Covalent single-bonded radii, Å

Be 0.9		B ...	
Mg ...		Al ...	Zr ...
Ca ...	Sc ...	Ga ...	Hf ...

Does this confirm or disprove the postulates of **F2.37–F2.39**?

A2.39 Confirm. While the same effect occurs in the case of ionic radii, the position is complicated by the changing valency through the series.

F2.40 As a last point it should be noted that we have been dealing with pairs of covalently, or ionically, bonded atoms. Atoms which do not undergo bonding, e.g. 2 Ar atoms, still experience a strong _____ when they approach closely, i.e. the atoms have a "size". The radius at which this occurs is called the **van der Waals radius** of the atom, after the Dutch scientist who first reported such interactions. This represents the volume in which the electrons are largely contained, and thus will always be *smaller/larger* than the covalent radius of the atom.

- -

> **A2.40** Interaction; larger, e.g. Cl, covalent radius 0.99Å; van der Waals radius 1.80Å.

Now repeat the programme test on p. 15, and mark it as before. If you score greater than 25 you have successfully completed this programme.

Summary

1. The larger the principal quantum number of an electron the further the electron is likely to be from the nucleus. It follows that atomic size increases with the principal quantum number of the valence electrons, i.e. with the position of the element in the group of the periodic table.

2. The atomic and ionic radii cannot be precisely defined because electron distributions of the atoms are not hard and definite in extent or always spherical. The maximum value of the radial probability distribution corresponds to the Bohr radius, but does not equate to any empirical measure of size.

3. Radii may be determined empirically from interatomic distances (bond lengths) which are the sums of such radii. Bond lengths may be measured by X-ray diffraction, neutron diffraction, microwave spectra, dipole moments, infrared spectra, etc.

4. The character of the bonding affects the values derived for such radii, since in the case of ionic bonding the atoms are thought of as being present as ions; since ions have more or less valence electrons than their parent atoms, their radii differ. We therefore distinguish the ionic radius from the covalent (or metallic) radius.

5. It is also important to know the coordination number or whether any multiple covalent bonding is present in the compound from which a radius is measured. These factors affect the value of the radius and therefore the proper use of any data on radii is confined to similar compounds to those in which the values were measured. It follows that radii are not exactly additive, and the values given in any table are an arbitrary set selected for their self-consistency.

6. The further an electron is from the nucleus, the more weakly it is held. It follows that ionisation energy falls as atomic size increases, as does the numerical value of the electron affinity.

7. While it is easy to halve the interatomic distance between two like atoms, to obtain the covalent or metallic radius, the determination of ionic radii involves empirical rules for dividing up the interatomic distance.

8. The sizes of an atom A and its ions are related as follows: $A^{n+} < A^{+} < A < A^{-} < A^{n-}$ $(n \geqslant 2)$.

9. Atomic and ionic radii generally increase on descending a group and decrease in traversing a period of the periodic table (in order of increasing atomic number).

10. There are some exceptions produced by discontinuities at the start of filling a new set of orbitals. Thus Ga is about the same size as Al, and Hf is smaller than Zr. The former is caused by the filling of the d-shell between the two elements (d-block contraction) and the latter by the filling of the f-shell (lanthanide contraction).

11. With some exceptions, all anions are larger than all cations. The exceptions are Rb^{+}, Cs^{+}, Fr^{+} and Ra^{2+} which are larger than F^{-} (and sometimes H^{-}).

12. The coordination number of an ion is the number of nearest neighbour ions, and common values are 2, 3, 4, 6 and 8 which correspond to linear, trigonal, tetrahedral, octahedral and cubic stereochemistries.

13. Simple crystal structures are usually determined by the number of anions which can pack symmetrically around the cation while touching it. Certain critical lower limits of the radius ratio ($\rho = r_{cation}/r_{anion}$) can be calculated for each geometrical arrangement.

14. Atoms which are not bonded experience a strong repulsion when they approach closely, i.e. the atoms have a "size". The radius at which this occurs is called the van der Waals radius of the atom, and is larger than the covalent radius.

Chapter 3

Electronic Screening and Effective Nuclear Charge

Dr. D. E. Billing

Council for National Academic Awards, London WC1X 8BP

Prior Knowledge, Content and Aims

This programme is designed to supplement the study of ionisation energies and radii of the elements. Such a study relies, at many points, on the concept of effective nuclear charge, yet this concept is frequently not clarified.

Familiarity is assumed with the concept of the nuclear atom, with the relationship between the numbers of protons and electrons, with expressions for potential energy and forces between electrostatic charges, with types of orbitals and electronic configurations of atoms, with the periodic table, and with atomic energy levels and the principal quantum number.

The programme uses a heuristic approach to develop the ideas of effective nuclear charge and of screening, from a consideration of potential energy outside a charged sphere. Slater's rules, for calculating screening, are stated and applied to several atoms, which cover two periods and one group of the periodic table. An inspection of these results reveals periodic trends in nuclear charge, and these are found to underlie trends in ionisation energy and radius. Irregularities in these trends are predicted. The concept of effective nuclear charge is also applied to the development of the Allred-Rochow electronegativity expression, to Pauling's method for calculating ionic radii, to the preferential ionisation of 4s or 3d electrons, and to expressions for atomic energy levels, ionisation energies and X-ray lines.

For convenience, the programme is divided into three sections, and each should be attempted at one session.

Detailed Objectives

When you have completed this programme you should be able to:

1. Explain concisely why the outer electrons of an atom do not feel the full nuclear charge.

2. Write down a relationship between actual nuclear charge, screening and effective nuclear charge, and explain why perfect screening is never achieved.

3. Give a qualitative account of Slater's rules for calculating the value of the screening parameter, and use these rules in order to calculate the effective nuclear charge.

4. Explain concisely why 4s electrons ionise before 3d electrons, although s electrons are less shielded than are d electrons by the same inner shell.

5. Describe the periodic variations in effective nuclear charge (Z^*) and select, from a series of elements, that of highest Z^* value.

6. Give two fundamental physical quantities which depend on Z^*, explain the nature of the dependence and describe the periodic trends in these quantities.

7. Describe the dependences of electronegativity, ionic radius and electronic energy on effective nuclear charge.

Programme Test

Before starting the programme itself, try the following test. Answers and scores are on p. 91. If you score greater than 27 you do not need to study the programme.

1. Explain concisely why the outer electrons of an atom do not feel the full nuclear charge.

2. Write down a relationship between the actual nuclear charge and the effective nuclear charge, Z^*.

3. What value would Z^* have in the case of perfect screening?

4. Explain concisely why perfect screening is never achieved.

5. Write down approximate Slater values for contributions to σ from the following types of electrons.
    (a) Outside the chosen one;
    (b) In the same group as the chosen one
    (c) Deep inside the chosen one

6. Are inner electrons shielded more or less than outer electrons?

7. State briefly why d or f electrons are more shielded than are s or p electrons, by the same inner shell.

8. Do 4s or 3d electrons feel the smaller value of Z^*, and which therefore ionise first? Why?

9. When moving from left to right in a period, does Z^* (a) increase; (b) decrease; or (c) remain about the same?

10. When descending a group of the periodic table, does Z^* (a) increase; (b) decrease; or (c) remain about the same?

11. Which of each of the following pairs of elements has the highest Z^* value?
    (a) Mg or S   (b) Cr or Ni   (c) Cs or Na

12. State briefly why ionisation energies and atomic radii depend on Z^*.

13. Indicate with arrows the directions in which ionisation energies and radii increase on the following representations of the usual periodic table.

14. After which two first transition series elements are there discontinuities in all these trends?

15. Which electronegativity scale is related, and by what relationship, to Z^*?

16. Explain briefly how Pauling used values of Z^* to calculate ionic radii from measured interionic distances.

17. To which function of the effective nuclear charge and the effective principal quantum number is the energy of an electron directly related?

PART 1

Other programmes or texts deal with ionisation energies and sizes of atoms. Since much of chemistry depends on these two quantities, it is important to understand how and why they vary in a periodic fashion.

One of the most important underlying factors in such variations is the nuclear charge which the outermost electrons actually "feel". We shall see that this is not the full nuclear charge, but it is reduced by the "screening" effect of the inner electrons. This screening and the "effective" nuclear charge resulting from it are therefore most important quantities in determining chemistry.

We first summarise definitions of ionisation energy and radius.

(a) If an atom is supplied with sufficient energy, it will lose its most weakly bound electron and become singly ionised.

$$A \rightarrow A^+ + e^-$$

The energy *absorbed* when one gram atom of gaseous atoms *loses* the outermost electron from each atom is referred to as its first ionisation energy, E_i.

(b) The radius of an atom (A) is conveniently measured by half the length of the single bond in the molecule A_2 or in some other molecule with a single A–A bond, or in the metal A. Radii of ions (A^+ or A^-) are similarly determined from measured distances in ionic structures. This is a matter of convenience, since in fact we know that neither atoms nor ions are hard spheres of constant size. Their effective sizes are determined by the distribution of electron density of the outermost electrons.

(c) We require to use the concept of potential energy due to electrostatic interactions. The potential energy (V) due to two charges q_1 and q_2 at a distance apart of d is given by

$$V = \frac{q_1 \times q_2}{d} \qquad \left[V = \frac{q_1 \times q_2}{4\pi\epsilon_0 d} \text{ in SI units} \right]$$

(d) We also require to remember that the potential energy felt by a charged particle some distance from a charged sphere is due to the *total* charge within that sphere acting as if concentrated at the *centre* of the sphere. Thus the potential V due to a charge of q_1 at a distance d from the centre of a sphere containing charges q_2 and q_3 is given by

$$V = \frac{q_1 \times (q_2 + q_3)}{d} \qquad \left[V = \frac{q_1 \times (q_2 + q_3)}{4\pi\epsilon_0 d} \quad \text{in SI units} \right]$$

The Concepts of Effective Nuclear Charge and Screening

F3.1 Consider an ion with Z protons (charge $+Ze$) in the nucleus and one electron (charge $-e$) in an s orbital.

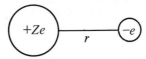

At a time when the electron is distance r from the nucleus, the potential energy of the system will be $V =$ _____ .

- -

A3.1 $V = \dfrac{-Ze^2}{r}$ $\qquad \left[V = \dfrac{-Ze^2}{4\pi\epsilon_0 r} \quad \text{in SI units} \right]$

F3.2 Consider now an *atom* with Z protons in the nucleus. How many extranuclear electrons does it have?

- -

A3.2 Z.

F3.3 If we assume a spherical electron distribution for all electrons, then we can draw an imaginary sphere, concentric with the nucleus, to exclude most of the electron density of the *outermost* electron, but to include most of the electron density of the *inner* electrons. How many inner electrons are there in a neutral atom?

- -

A3.3 $(Z - 1)$.

F3.4 This sphere will then include a positive charge due to the nucleus, and a negative charge due to the inner electrons. What is the charge in the nucleus? What is the charge of the total number of *inner* electrons?

- -

A3.4 $(+Ze)$; $[-(Z - 1)e]$.

F3.5 The potential outside a charged sphere is due to the *total* charge within it.

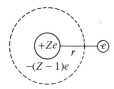

Look at the diagram and write down the potential energy V felt by the *outermost* electron at radius r.

A3.5
$$V = \frac{-e \times [+Ze - (Z-1)e]}{r} = \frac{-e^2}{r} \qquad \left[V = \frac{-e^2}{4\pi\epsilon_0 r} \quad \text{in SI units} \right]$$

F3.6 Thus, instead of the actual nuclear charge of $+Ze$, the *outermost* electron will only feel the influence of an *effective nuclear charge* of $+Z^*e =$ _____.

A3.6 $+Z^*e = +e$.

F3.7 We say that the inner electrons have "screened" or "shielded" the outermost electron from the full nuclear charge. Another way of saying the same thing is that the outermost electron feels a repulsion from the inner electrons, and this partially counteracts the attraction of the nucleus. Generally, the effective nuclear charge is given by
$$Z^*e = (Z - \sigma)e$$
where σ is the "screening constant" (or "shielding constant") and in this case is equal to $\sigma =$ _____.

A3.7 $(Z - 1)$.

F3.8 In this case, due to the assumptions (i) that there is spherical electron distribution for all electrons and (ii) that all electron density due to the inner electrons is within the imaginary sphere while the outermost electron is entirely outside the sphere, perfect screening of the outermost electron by the inner electrons has been achieved.

F3.9 Neither of these assumptions is correct since electrons are in orbitals, distributed over all space, rather than in fixed orbits, and not all of these are spherical. Give some examples of orbitals which are *not* spherical.

A3.9 2p, 3p, 3d, 4f, etc., i.e. any orbital except an s orbital.

F3.10 Hence screening is never perfect and σ, the screening parameter, differs from $(Z - 1)$. Is σ always lower or higher than $(Z - 1)$?

A3.10 Lower.

PART 2

Calculation of the Screening Parameter

F3.11 Slater has given some rules for calculating σ. First, divide the electrons of an atom into the respective orbital groups.

> 1s
> 2s and 2p
> 3s and 3p
> 3d
> 4s and 4p
> 4d
> 4f
> 5s and 5p
> 6s and 6p etc.

Thus for the silicon atom, how many electrons do we have in these groups?

A3.11 2, 8, 4, 0, etc. since Si is $1s^2 2s^2 2p^6 3s^2 3p^2$.

F3.12 Secondly, pick *one* electron for which the shielding is to be calculated. For example, we calculate σ for one of the silicon electrons in the 3s + 3p group. Lastly, add up the contributions to σ for the *other* electrons, according to the following scheme.

Type of electron	*Contribution to σ for each electron of this type*
All electrons in groups outside chosen one	0
All other electrons in same group as chosen one	0.35 (or 0.30 for 1s electrons)
All electrons in *shell* immediately inside	0.85 (or 1.00*)
All electrons further inside	1.00

*1.00 for the next orbital *group*, *if* the *chosen* electron is in a d or f orbital. Note that the shell includes all groups with the same principal quantum number.

Thus for each silicon 3p electron, $\sigma =$ _____ .

A3.12 $\sigma = (3 \times 0.35) + (8 \times 0.85) + (2 \times 1.00) = 9.85$.

F3.13 Hence this electron feels $Z^* =$ _____ .

A3.13 $Z^* = (Z - \sigma) = (14 - 9.85) = 4.15$.

F3.14 We are often, as above, interested in the valence electrons, but we could equally choose to calculate the screening for an inner electron, say a 2p silicon electron, In this case $\sigma =$ _____ . Hence $Z^* =$ _____ .

A3.14 $\sigma = (7 \times 0.35) + (2 \times 0.85) = 4.15; Z^* = 9.85$.

F3.15 Having used the table in **F3.12**, we go on to notice some facts about it. Electrons further out than the chosen one are beyond our imaginary sphere (**F3.5**). What value do they each contribute to σ? Are, then, the inner electrons shielded more or less than outer electrons?

    A3.15 Zero; less.

F3.16 Are the electrons in the same orbital group as the chosen one as effective in screening as inner electrons or not? About how effective are they compared with the inner electrons? (See **F3.12**.)

    A3.16 No; only about one third as effective.

F3.17 Are d or f electrons more or less shielded than s or p electrons (by the same inner shell)? (See **F3.12**.)

    A3.17 More; this is due to the poor penetration of d and f orbitals towards the nucleus.

F3.18 We take a further example. Bismuth has the electronic configuration _____

    A3.18 $1s^2\,2s^2\,2p^6\,3s^2\,3p^6\,3d^{10}\,4s^2\,4p^6\,4d^{10}\,4f^{14}\,5s^2\,5p^6\,5d^{10}\,6s^2\,6p^3$.

F3.19 Hence, for each valence electron, in bismuth $\sigma = $ _____. Then $Z^* = $ _____.

    A3.19 $\sigma = (4 \times 0.35) + (0.85 \times 18) + (1.00 \times 60) = 76.70$.
    $Z^* = (83 - 76.70) = 6.30$.

Trends in Effective Nuclear Charge
F3.20 Let us see what periodic trends can be found for Z^*. Calculate Z^* for the valence electrons of just *one* of the elements of the period Li–Ne.

    A3.20 Li 1.30; Be 1.95; B 2.60; C 3.25; N 3.90; O 4.55; F 5.20; Ne 5.85.

F3.21 As we move from left to right across the period is the actual nuclear charge increasing faster or slower than the screening due to electrons in the same shell? In fact for each increase of the atomic number by one (within this period), the increment in Z^* is $\Delta Z^* = $ _____ .

    A3.21 Faster; $\Delta Z^* = (1.00 - 0.35) = 0.65$.

F3.22 This is true of any period (although there are discontinuities due to the transition metals). Thus for the elements K to As (for the 4s electrons) we have $Z^* =$ _____. (Work out Z^* for any *one* of this series.)

A3.22 K 2.20; Ca 2.85; Sc 3.00; Ti 3.15; V 3.30; Cr 2.95; Mn 3.60; Fe 3.75; Co 3.90; Ni 4.05; Cu 3.70; Zn 4.35; Ga 5.00; Ge 5.65; As 6.30.

F3.23 Looking at these data, we see that Z^* falls after which two elements? This is followed by a larger increase in each case. The fall is associated with the $3d^5 4s^1$ and $3d^{10} 4s^1$ configurations of which elements?

A3.23 V and Ni; Cr and Cu.

F3.24 For a vertical group of the periodic table there are other trends. Thus for the alkali metals, $Z^* =$ _____. (Work out Z^* for any *one* of this series.)

A3.24 Li 1.30; Na 2.20; K 2.20; Rb 2.20; Cs 2.20; Fr 2.20.

F3.25 Look at the data for Na to Fr. As we descend the group, does Z^* generally increase, decrease or remain approximately constant?

Hence for a vertical group does the actual nuclear charge generally increase faster than, slower than, or at the same rate as the screening? (The first member may be atypical.)

A3.25 Approximately constant; at the same rate.

PART 3

Applications of the Concept of Effective Nuclear Charge
(a) Radii and ionisation energies
F3.26 Consider the variation of Z^* across a horizontal period such as Li–Ne. This will have an effect on the force holding the outermost electron to the nucleus. As the atomic number increases within a period, will the strength of binding of the valence electrons increase, decrease or remain about the same?

A3.26 Increase.

F3.27 Will this cause the atomic radius (and consequently the ionic radii) to increase or decrease? Will the energy required to remove the valence electrons (the ionisation energy) increase or decrease?

A3.27 Decrease; increase.

F3.28 Thus the radii tend to decrease and the ionisation energies tend to increase in moving across a horizontal period from left to right.

There will be certain irregularities in these trends due to those in Z^*. Thus there is a discontinuity around Cr (see **F3.23**).

Will the first ionisation potential of vanadium be much less than, much greater than, or about the same as that of chromium?

A3.28 About the same.

F3.29 Similarly, will the atomic radii rise or fall across the first transition series? After nickel there is a slight increase or decrease. Which?

A3.29 Fall; increase.

F3.30 For the alkali metals, we saw in **F3.24–25** that Z^* is approximately constant, but there is a second factor.

The radius at which the valence electrons have their maximum electron density depends on the principal quantum number. Does this radius increase or decrease as the atomic number increases?

A3.30 Increase.

F3.31 This second factor is dominant. Do radii therefore increase or decrease as the atomic number rises within the periodic group? Do ionisation energies increase or decrease in descending a group?

A3.31 Increase; decrease.

Z^* cannot usually be used to predict irregularities, since Slater's rules are only approximations and since the form of the radial part of the wave function and electron pairing energies are also involved. In addition, ionisation energy depends on radius as well as on Z^*.

(b) Electronegativities

F3.32 What will be the force on an electron in a molecule due to an atom, if the atom is of effective nuclear charge Z^* and the electron is assumed to be at a distance r, equal to the atomic (covalent) radius? Allred and Rochow used this as a measure of the electron attracting power of an atom in a molecule (electronegativity).

A3.32 Z^*e^2/r^2 $[Z^*e^2/4\pi\epsilon_0 r^2$ in SI units] .

(c) Measurement of ionic radii

F3.33 Does ionic radius depend on Z^* or $1/Z^*$?

A3.33 $1/Z^*$.

F3.34 Pauling therefore gave the following expresssion for the ionic radius, $r = C_n/Z^*$, where C_n is a constant for a particular isoelectronic sequence. Hence by using the ratio of the radii of Na^+ and F^-, we calculate from the Na–F distance of 2.31Å in sodium fluoride, the values $r_{Na^+} = $ _____ and $r_{F^-} = $ _____ .

(Note: $C_n = rZ^*$ is the same for Na^+ and F^- since they are isoelectronic, therefore first calculate Z^*.)

A3.34 $Z^*_{Na^+}/Z^*_{F^-} = 6.85/4.85 = r_{F^-}/r_{Na^+}$ (since Na^+ and F^- are isoelectronic) and $r_{Na^+} + r_{F^-} = 2.31$Å. Therefore, $r_{Na^+} = 0.96$Å and $r_{F^-} = 1.35$Å.

(d) Order of energies of orbitals

F3.35 For vanadium, the 4s electrons were found (F3.22) to feel an effective nuclear charge of 3.30. The calculation of Z^* for the 3d electrons gives $Z^* = $ _____ .

A3.35 4.30.

F3.36 Do the 4s electrons feel a greater or a smaller effective nuclear charge than the 3d electrons? Will the 4s electrons ionise more or less readily than 3d electrons?

A3.36 Smaller; more.

(e) Calculation of ionisation energies

F3.37 The energy level of any electron is given approximately by

$$E = \frac{-2me^4\pi^2}{h^2}\left(\frac{Z^*}{n^*}\right)^2 = -1310 \times \left(\frac{Z^*}{n^*}\right)^2 \text{ kJ mol}^{-1}$$

where m is the mass of the electron, and n^* is the "effective" principal quantum number and takes the following values for different values of n, the principal quantum number:

n	1	2	3	4	5	6
n^*	1	2	3	3.7	4	4.2

When complete ionisation of an electron has occurred, what is its value of n? In this case, from the above expression, $E = $ _____ .

A3.37 n is infinite; similarly n^* is infinite. $E = 0$.

F3.38 In order to ionise, an electron must be excited from a level of given n to the level where n is infinite. Hence the ionisation energy, E_i, of an electron is the difference between $E = 0$ and the above expressions for E, i.e. $E_i = $ _____ .

A3.38 $E_i = +1310\,(Z^*/n^*)^2$ kJ mol^{-1}.

F3.39 Hence using this expression, give a rough plot of $\sqrt{E_i}$ against Z for the iso-electronic series Li, Be$^+$, B^{2+}, C^{3+}.

(Note: for each species first work out Z^*.)

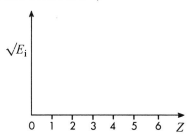

A3.39 Since the species are isoelectronic, σ is constant and is in fact the intercept on the Z axis.

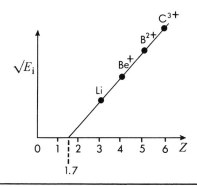

(f) X-ray spectroscopy

F3.40 Another method of measuring σ and Z^* is by means of X-ray spectroscopy. By taking differences of energy levels in **F3.37** we obtain $\Delta E = E_1 - E_2 =$ _____.
Such energy quanta typically give absorptions in the X-ray spectral region.

A3.40
$$\Delta E = 1310(Z^*)^2 \left[\frac{1}{(n_2^*)^2} - \frac{1}{(n_1^*)^2} \right] \text{ kJ mol}^{-1}$$

F3.41 The K_α X-ray line is considered to be due to an electron falling from the second quantum shell ($n_1 = 2 = n_1^*$) to the first quantum shell ($n_2 = 1 = n_2^*$) to replace an electron ejected from there in electron bombardment of the surface. Hence the K_α line of iron occurs at $\Delta E =$ _____ kJ mol^{-1}.

(Note: take $\sigma = 1.00$ for *both* shells.)

A3.41 $\Delta E = 1310 \times (26 - 1)^2 \times (1/1^2 - 1/2^2) = 6.14 \times 10^5$ kJ mol^{-1}.

Now repeat the programme test on p. 26, and mark it as before. If you score greater than 27 you have successfully completed this programme.

Summary

1. An outer electron does not feel the full nuclear charge due to the screening caused by inner electrons.

2. The effective nuclear charge is $Z^*e = (Z - \sigma)e$.

3. Slater gave rules for calculating contributions to the screening (σ) felt by any given electron, thus allowing Z^* to be calculated. Outer electrons contribute nothing; those in the same orbital group contribute about one third as much as inner electrons. Each inner electron almost completely counterbalances the effect of one proton in the nucleus.

4. d and f electrons are more shielded than s or p electrons, by the same inner shell.

5. Z^* increases from left to right in a period, causing ionisation energy to increase and radius to decrease.

6. Z^* is approximately constant within a group, allowing the increased radius to cause a decrease in ionisation energy (as the group is descended).

7. There are irregularities within these trends, associated with the transition metals.

8. The Allred-Rochow expression relates electron attracting power of an atom to Z^* and to the covalent radius ($x = Z^*e^2/r^2$).

9. Pauling divided interionic distances in the inverse ratio of the effective nuclear charges, to obtain ionic radii.

10. 4s electrons are ionised more easily than 3d electrons.

11. The energy level of an electron is related to the square of Z^*, and to the inverse square of the effective principal quantum number. The ionisation energy is similarly related. $E_i = +1310(Z^*/n^*)^2$ kJ mol^{-1}.

12. Energies of K_α X-ray spectral lines are obtained by assuming that $\sigma = 1.00$.

Chapter 4

Ionisation Energies and Electron Affinities

Dr. I. A. Ellis

Westfield College, University of London, London NW3 7ST

Introduction

This programme is written to build on the concepts concerning the size and constitution of atoms and ions and the arrangement of elements in the periodic table. It is assumed that the periodic arrangement of elements will be related to quantum theory and that the student will be familiar with electron shells composed of orbitals of differing sizes and shapes.

The programme contains an introduction to and definitions of ionisation energy (E_i) and electron affinity (E_a). Values of E_i are related to chemical reactivity on a qualitative and semi-quantitative basis, and the idea of a limit to the energy involved in a chemical change is introduced. Reactivity leads to the concepts of valence and oxidation number and their connection with E_i. It is also shown that values of E_i may be used to relate different chemical systems, hence to give a guide to reactivity and possibly to predict products. In addition, the variations in E_i are related to fundamental changes in electronic structures, and finally some uses of E_i values in other areas are considered.

Objectives

1. To define ionisation energy and electron affinity.

2. To relate reactivity to ionisation energy.

3. To establish a relationship between chemical reactivity and the formation of highly charged entities.

4. To relate valency and oxidation number to ionisation energies.

5. To outline the effects of electron shielding on atomic size and reactivity.

6. To apply ionisation energy to molecules.

7. To introduce lattice energies and electrode potentials.

Programme Test

Before starting the programme itself, try the following test. Answers and scores are on p. 92. If you score greater than 20 you do not need to study the programme.

1. What is the ionisation energy of a species?
2. Some species react by losing their electrons. Relate their reactivity to their ionisation energies.
3. Where it is very difficult to remove electrons from a species, describe the usual alternative.
4. Given the values of E_i for Ca (see the tables on pp. 82–85) describe how it will react.
5. Consider how the concept of valency may prove useful.
6. Tl^{3+} is highly oxidising, giving Tl^+. Predict the stability of the ionic compound, TlH_3.
7. Explain the differing reactivities of H^- and F^- ions.
8. How will Si^{4+} behave in aqueous solution?
9. Relate the compounds NaO_2 and O_2PtF_6 to each other and to the O_2 molecule.
10. Relate the E_i values of C to those of B and N (see the tables, pp. 82–85).
11. Why are K atoms larger than those of Na?
12. Explain why K atoms are also larger than the atoms of Sc, Ti, Ga or Ge.
13. Explain why the increase in size between Li and Na atoms is greater than that between Rb and Cs.
14. What are the two main factors affecting lattice energies?
15. Give the relationship between electrode potentials and equilibrium constants.

F4.1 Atoms in their reactions interact via their *most/least* energetic electrons.

- -

    A4.1 Most. The electrons having the greatest amount of energy will be the ones most likely to escape from complete dependence on the nucleus. The outer electrons of an atom therefore govern its chemistry. Hence, a guide to the reactivity of an atom may be acquired by measuring the energy associated with these electrons.

F4.2 An atom of sodium has two electrons more than that of fluorine. When the two atoms react, sodium loses an electron to fluorine and they both attain the same electronic configuration, with the formation of the ionic compound NaF. In this the ion Na^+ will be *larger/smaller* than the ion F^-.

- -

    A4.2 Smaller.

F4.3 The ions in an ionic compound will tend to be displaced in an electric field. When allowed to move, the positive ions will travel towards the negatively charged cathode and are called cations while the negative ions will go to the anode which is *positively/negatively* charged and are called anions.

- -

    A4.3 Positively.

F4.4 With the exception of H^+, ions encountered in chemical reactions will be like atoms in that they consist of a small, dense, positively charged _____ surrounded by a large, diffuse, cloud of negative _____ .

A4.4 Nucleus; electrons.

F4.5 Some atoms react by *gaining/losing* electrons to form cations.

A4.5 Losing.

F4.6 The energy required to remove completely the most loosely bound electron from a gaseous atom in its lowest energy state is called the **first ionisation energy** (first ionisation potential). The ionisation energy, E_i, of hydrogen is $13.60 \text{ eV} = 1310$ kJ mol^{-1} (1 eV $\equiv$ 96.5 kJ). Hydrogen of course *can/cannot* have a second ionisation energy.

A4.6 Cannot. Since hydrogen atoms have only one electron they can have no second E_i.

The second E_i is the energy associated with the reaction $M^+ \rightarrow M^{2+} + e^-$ and similarly for subsequent E_i's.

F4.7 Some atoms react by adding electrons to form _____ .

A4.7 Anions.

F4.8 The **electron affinity**, E_a, of an atom may be defined as the energy released when an electron is added to a neutral gaseous atom in its ground state. The E_a of fluorine is $+3.46 \text{ eV} \equiv 334$ kJ mol^{-1}. However, only the halogens normally form anions with the release of energy and thus many E_a's have *positive/negative* values.

A4.8 Negative. This means that energy must be supplied to form such anions. Experimentally, E_a's are difficult to determine and E_i's are easier. Hence, we will concentrate on the latter.

F4.9 The first E_i of an atom is a measure of the energy associated with its *most/least* energetic electron. This electron will the the one most likely to take part in a chemical change and the one *nearest/farthest* from the nucleus.

A4.9 Most; farthest.

F4.10 The second E_i is the energy associated with the removal of the most loosely bound electron from the species produced by the loss of the first electron, and similarly for third, fourth and subsequent E_i's. Due to electrostatic laws subsequent E_i's will become progressively *larger/smaller.*

A4.10 Larger.

F4.11 Similarly in considering E_a's. As the charge on the anion becomes progressively more negative, it will become energetically *more/less* favourable to add further electrons .

A4.11 Less. E_a for O to O^- is +142 kJ mol^{-1} and for O^- to O^{2-} it is −701 kJ mol^{-1}.

F4.12 The energy required to remove a single electron from an atom is quite high and quickly increases for subsequent electrons. Use the tables at the end of the book (pp. 82–85) to calculate the energy required to produce Li^{3+}. Give your answer in kJ mol^{-1}.

A4.12 $E = 19,610$ kJ mol^{-1} (1st E_i + 2nd E_i + 3rd E_i).

An example of a very exothermic reaction is $2Al + 1\frac{1}{2}O_2 = Al_2O_3$ with just over 1680 kJ mol^{-1} evolved.

It can therefore be seen that the formation of highly charged ions will be too energy consuming for chemical reactions to produce them.

F4.13 Lithium, on the left of the periodic table, is a reactive metal which readily loses an electron to give _____ . Fluorine, on the right of the table, will _____ an electron to give F^-.

A4.13 Li^+; add. There are thus competing processes which decide whether an atom will become a cation, an anion or share its electrons in a covalent bond. These processes may be related to the relative values of E_i.

F4.14 The number of electrons an atom uses in a chemical reaction represents its valency or combining power. The unique nature of hydrogen arises because it may gain or lose only one electron in its reactions. Hence the valency of hydrogen is *one/two/three.*

A4.14 One.

F4.15 Thus the number of hydrogen atoms or their equivalent with which an atom of an element will combine is the _____ of the element.

A4.15 Valency. Note that while some elements have a unique valency some have several different valencies and maximum valency is always closely related to an element's E_i's.

F4.16 Give the valencies of the elements other than hydrogen in the following species:
(a) HF; (b) GeH$_4$; (c) BF$_3$; (d) NH$_4$$^+$; (e) ReH$_9$$^{2-}$.

- -

   A4.16 (a) 1; (b) 4; (c) 3 and 1; (d) 3; (e) 7.

F4.17 From the values in the table of E_i's (pp. 82–85), lithium will react with hydrogen to form the ionic compound LiH composed of ＿＿＿ and ＿＿＿ ions.

- -

   A4.17 Li$^+$, H$^-$. In this compound the **oxidation number** of lithium is +1.
   Indeed lithium exhibits no other oxidation numbers, whereas hydrogen may
   have an oxidation number of +1 or −1. Hence, the oxidation number is the
   number of electrons which must be added to or taken from an ion or
   combined atom to produce a neutral species.

F4.18 Certain atoms will have unique oxidation numbers, e.g. F −1; O −2; K +1;
Ca +2; while others will have variable oxidation numbers. These will be related to the
E_i's of the atoms. Give the oxidation numbers of the atoms in:
(a) BaF$_2$;   (b) SiF$_4$;   (c) BaSiO$_3$.

- -

   A4.18 (a) +2 and −1; (b) +4 and −1; (c) +2, +4 and −2.
   Note: oxidation numbers are often denoted by Roman numerals.

F4.19 The H$^-$ ion is endothermic to the extent of 145 kJ mol^{-1} with respect to ½H$_2$.
This means 145 kJ are required to form one mole and will be available if and when it
reacts. Hence, H$^-$ ions are usually *stable/unstable* with respect to reaction.

- -

   A4.19 Unstable. The energy released when they react drives their reactions
   essentially to completion.

F4.20 Hydride ions usually react by abstracting a proton and forming hydrogen gas.
What else will be produced when hydride ions react with:
(a) HCl;   (b) H$_2$O;   (c) NH$_3$?

- -

   A4.20 (a) Cl$^-$; (b) OH$^-$; (c) NH$_2$$^-$.

F4.21 The formation of F$^-$ is exothermic by 334 kJ mol^{-1} with respect to F atoms.
This means 334 kJ mol^{-1} will be required to transform it and therefore F$^-$ will be
reactive/unreactive.

- -

   A4.21 Unreactive.

F4.22 Values of E_i supply a direct measure of electron loss but they also provide evidence for stability in certain favoured electron configurations. Where E_i's are high and an atom has a few electrons less than a favoured electron configuration, electrons may be *lost/gained*.

A4.22 Gained. Therefore E_i's will also act as a guide to electron gain and hence electron affinities.

F4.23 For many chemical reactions the surplus energy driving them is of the order of 400 kJ mol^{-1}. Hence, under chemical conditions, since all ions are a source of energy, highly charged species *are/are not* formed.

A4.23 Are not.

F4.24 Thus N^{3-} is very reactive and in the presence of water yields OH⁻ and _____. Similarly O^{2-} ions will react with water to give _____.

A4.24 NH_3; OH⁻.

F4.25 In general, cations with charges greater than +2 are uncommon although species with charges up to +4 may be found in the isolation of ionic crystals. In solution, species with a high charge may react with the solvent. Thus on evaporating an aqueous solution of $AlCl_3$ to dryness, Al_2O_3 will be left and _____ is given off.

A4.25 HCl. This is due to reaction of Al^{3+} with H_2O, also called hydrolysis.

F4.26 Li with a first E_i of 520 kJ mol^{-1} is reactive, Cu with a first E_i of 755 kJ mol^{-1} is unreactive, and Au with a first E_i of 895 kJ mol^{-1} is very unreactive indeed. Hence He with a first E_i of 2380 kJ mol^{-1} will be *reactive/inert*.

A4.26 Inert. Remember we are considering *chemical* reactions.

F4.27 Also from the table of E_i's (pp. 82–85), boron will have a valency of _____ and with the uniquely divalent oxygen will combine to form _____.

A4.27 Three; B_2O_3.

F4.28 Where similarities in E_i's occur in different elements, reactivities will be similar. Consider the values of the 1st to 5th E_i's of silicon and titanium. If Si forms the compounds SiS_2 and $SiCl_4$, what compounds will Ti form with oxygen and fluorine?

A4.28 TiO_2, TiF_4.

F4.29 From the table of E_i's (pp. 82—85) it can be seen that for systems of similar electron configuration in the same period, e.g. B to N, as nuclear charge increases the E_i's *increase/decrease*.

— —

A4.29 Increase.

F4.30 This increase of E_i's with the addition of electrons of the same type is fairly general throughout horizontal periods in the periodic table. The effect, however, is *larger/smaller* in transition series, where *inner/outer* orbitals are being filled, than in the main group elements.

— —

A4.30 Smaller, inner. Compare this effect in the series Al to Ar and Sc to Ni.

F4.31 The effects of the relationships in **F4.29** and **F4.30** can be seen in the relative sizes of atoms. Thus in size, Na > Mg > Al and Mn > Fe > Co > Ni. This is a decrease in atomic radius with increasing atomic number and is the result of an overall *decrease/ increase* in effective nuclear charge.

— —

A4.31 Increase.

F4.32 This decrease in size with increasing atomic number is usually counteracted when electrons are forced to enter higher quantum levels. Thus if we compare elements in the vertical groups, e.g. Li, Na, K, Rb, Cs, sizes will normally *increase/decrease*.

— —

A4.32 Increase. In general, as nuclear charge increases in a group, atomic size increases and valence electrons move further from the nucleus.

F4.33 The extent to which valence electrons penetrate an electron cloud will affect E_i's, and so E_i's will depend on the type of electron removed. For electrons with the same principal quantum number, p electrons will, on average, be farther from the nucleus than s electrons. Thus such s electrons will be more penetrating than p electrons. Therefore, in the case of the first E_i's of Be ($1s^2 2s^2$) and B ($1s^2 2s^2 2p^1$), the outer electron of B will be *more/less* penetrating than that of Be and a *decrease/ increase* in E_i may be anticipated.

— —

A4.33 Less, decrease; Using the same arguments the order of penetrating power is s > p > d > f. Also, of course, an electron which penetrates less is better shielded.

F4.34 Note the E_i's of As, Sb and Bi in the tables (pp. 82—85). Arsenic forms the compounds As_2O_3 and AsF_5. Write down the possible chlorides and sulphides of Bi.

— —

A4.34 $BiCl_3$, $BiCl_5$, Bi_2S_3, Bi_2S_5. Note that As also forms the compounds AsF_3 and As_2O_5. The valencies III and V are not exclusive to any ligand. Note further that $BiCl_5$ and Bi_2S_5 have not been recorded, as Bi^V is only formed with difficulty. This, however, cannot be predicted from values of E_i.

F4.35 The 1st and 2nd E_i's of NO are 890 kJ mol^{-1} and > 4800 kJ mol^{-1}. Suggest a likely product of reaction between NO and Cl_2.

A4.35 NOCl.

The concepts of E_i and E_a are just as applicable to molecules or radicals as they are to atoms.

F4.36 The O_2 gas molecule has values for the 1st and 2nd E_i's of 1180 and > 6800 kJ mol^{-1}. With PtF_6 it forms the compound O_2PtF_6 containing O_2^+ and PtF_6^- ions. Anticipate the reaction of Xe, having 1st and 2nd E_i's of 1170 and 5800 kJ mol^{-1} with PtF_6.

A4.36 The product is $XePtF_6$, the original "inert" gas compound.

F4.37 The lattice energy of a crystal, U, is the energy given out, i.e. lost by the system, when one mole of an ionic crystal is formed from its constituent ions in the gas phase, e.g. in the reaction Na^+ (g) + Cl^- (g) → NaCl (s), $\Delta H = -U$. Lattice energies will be different for different ions and different lattices, and are hard to obtain experimentally. They may, however, be calculated. The two main factors affecting lattice energies, since these depend on electrostatic attractions, are the size and charge of ions. The smaller the ions the *larger/smaller* the lattice energy. The greater the charge on the ion the *larger/smaller* the lattice energy.

A4.37 Larger; larger.

F4.38 In an ionic solid, the heat of formation will numerically equal $(-U)$ minus E_a for the anion-forming species plus E_i for the cation-forming species plus whatever energies are required to produce the gaseous atoms for which values of E_i and _____ are derived.

A4.38 E_a. Thus for sodium chloride,
$$\Delta H_f(NaCl) = -U(NaCl) + E_i(Na) - E_a(Cl) + \Delta H_{sublimation}(Na) + \tfrac{1}{2}\Delta H_{dissociation}(Cl_2).$$
This relationship, which forms the basis of the Born-Haber cycle, provides a way of evaluating E_a, as U may be calculated and the other quantities are known from experiment.

F4.39 The inherent tendency to lose or gain electrons is the electrical driving force in a system. This may be expressed as an electric potential which is a measure of overall reactivity. These potentials are measured in volts relative to hydrogen.

E^0 for $H^+ + e^- \rightarrow \frac{1}{2}H_2$ is defined as zero.

E^0 is the standard electrode potential for a molar solution; on this basis, in molar acid solution:

$$Na^+ + e^- \rightarrow Na; \qquad E^0 = -2.71 \text{ V};$$
$$\frac{1}{2}F_2 + e^- \rightarrow F^-; \qquad E^0 = +2.85 \text{ V}.$$

Using the tables of E_i values (pp. 82–85), E^0 for Rb will be *more/less* negative than that for Na, and E^0 for Br will be *smaller/larger* than that for F.

- -

> **A4.39** More, smaller. Rb is more reactive than Na, and Br is less reactive than F. This is an over-simplified picture, however, as heats of hydration also contribute to E^0.

F4.40 Electrode potentials are important as they are related to the equilibrium constant of a reaction. In fact,

$$E^0 = \frac{RT}{nF} \ln K$$

where E^0 is the standard electrode potential, R is the gas constant, T is the temperature in degrees Kelvin, n is the number of electrons involved, F is the Faraday constant, and K is the equilibrium constant for the reaction.

Now repeat the programme test on p. 37, and mark it as before. If you score greater than 20 you have successfully completed this programme.

Summary

1. Atoms in their reactions interact via their most energetic electrons. The electrons having the greatest amount of energy will be the ones most likely to escape from complete dependence on the nucleus. The outer electrons of an atom therefore govern its chemistry.

2. The energy required to remove completely the most loosely bound electron from a gaseous atom in its lowest energy state is called the first ionisation energy, E_i. All values of E_i are positive.

3. The second E_i is the energy associated with the reaction $M^+ \rightarrow M^{2+} + e^-$. Similar reactions lead to values for subsequent E_i's.

4. The electron affinity of an atom, E_a, may be defined as the energy released when an electron is added to a neutral gaseous atom in its ground state.

5. Only the halogens normally form anions with release of energy and therefore have positive values of E_a.

6. Due to electrostatic interactions, successive values of E_i and E_a will progressively become numerically larger.

7. The formation of highly-charged ions will consume too much energy for them to be produced in chemical reactions. If formed, highly-charged ions will be very reactive.

8. The number of electrons an atom uses in a chemical reaction represents its valency or combining power. The maximum valency is always closely related to the ionisation energies of an element.

9. The oxidation number is the number of electrons which must be added or taken from an ion or combined ion to produce a neutral species. The oxidation numbers which are feasible will be related to the ionisation energies of the atoms.

10. An element with high ionisation energies will be unreactive, as with the noble gases. Elements with similar E_i values will have similar reactivities. High values of E_i may be associated with electron gain, rather than loss, when a stable configuration can be formed by gain of electrons.

11. For species of similar electron configuration in the same period, E_i values increase with increase in nuclear charge. This effect is smaller in the transition series, where inner orbitals are being filled, than in the main group elements.

12. In general, as nuclear charge increases in a vertical group, atomic size increases and valence electrons move further from the nucleus.

13. The order of penetration of an electron cloud by valence electrons is $s > p > d > f$, and this affects the ionisation energies of the valence electrons.

14. The concepts of E_i and E_a are equally applicable to molecules or radicals as to atoms.

15. The lattice energy of a crystal is the energy given out when one mole of an ionic crystal is formed from its constituent ions in the gas phase. The two main factors affecting lattice energies, since these depend on electrostatic attractions, are the size and charge of ions. The smaller the ions and the greater the charge, the larger the lattice energy, U.

16. In an ionic solid, the heat of formation is equal to the sum of minus the lattice energy, plus the ionisation energy minus the electron affinity, and plus the energies required to convert the elements into gaseous atoms.

17. The inherent tendency to lose or gain electrons is the electrical driving force in a system, and may be expressed as the standard electrode potential, E^0 volts, for a molar solution measured relative to hydrogen. E^0 and E_i values are related.

18. Electrode potentials are related to the equilibrium constant of a reaction,

$$E^0 = \frac{RT}{nF} \ln K.$$

Chapter 5

Electronegativity

Dr. D. E. Billing

Council for National Academic Awards, London WC1X 8BP

Assumed Knowledge, Content and Aims

This programme concerns the distribution of electrons amongst the atoms of molecules.

A knowledge is assumed of electronic configurations, ionisation energies (sometimes called ionisation potentials) and electron affinities of atoms, and of the periodic variation of the last two quantities. The programme develops the concept of electron-attracting power from the ideas of ionisation energies and electron affinities and this leads to the Mulliken scale of electronegativity. The periodic variation of electronegativity is presented. The Pauling scale of electronegativity is developed from the effect of partial ionic character on bond energy, and the relationship with dipole moment is discussed. Finally some applications of the Pauling electronegativity scale to the understanding of hydrolysis mechanisms, hydrogen bonding and extent of ionic character are discussed.

For convenience, the programme is divided into three sections, each of which should be attempted at one session.

The method of treatment emphasises comprehension and discovery of relationships, rather than statement of relationships together with conditioned learning.

Detailed Objectives

When you have completed this programme you should be able to:

1. Explain concisely the meaning of the concept of electronegativity.

2. State to which fundamental physical quantities this concept is related, and distinguish it from such quantities.

3. Write down the relationships which define electronegativity as given by Mulliken and by Pauling.

4. Describe in qualitative terms the variation of electronegativity over the periodic table, and select the most electronegative from a series of elements which are horizontally or vertically related.

5. Give very approximate values for the Pauling electronegativities of representative elements.

6. Recognise physical quantities which are directly dependant on electro-
    negativity differences.

7. Explain briefly the manner of this dependence.

8. Use an understanding of electronegativity to make qualitative predictions
    about the course of simple reactions, about the strength of hydrogen bonding
    and about the bond character.

Programme Test

Before starting the programme itself, try the following test. Answers and scores are
on p. 93. If you score greater than 27 you do not need to study the programme.

1. Explain concisely the meaning of the concept of electronegativity.

2. On which one or more of the following physical quantities does the concept of
    electronegativity directly depend?
    (a) dipole moment   (b) electron affinity   (c) ionisation energy
    (d) ionic radius

3. Write down an equation which defines electronegativity as given by (a) Mulliken
    and (b) Pauling.

4. State briefly the distinction between electronegativity and electron affinity.

5. Which of the quantities in Mulliken's definition is usually the more important in
    determining the value of the electronegativity?

6. On the following representation of the conventional periodic table put arrows to
    indicate the directions in which the electronegativity increases.

```
┌──────────────────────────────┐
│ Li                        Ne  │
│                               │
│                               │
│ Fr                            │
└──────────────────────────────┘
```

7. Which element in each of the following series has the highest electronegativity?
    (a) sulphur, silicon, sodium;   (b) copper, chromium, calcium;
    (c) phosphorus, arsenic, antimony;   (d) boron, sulphur, tin.

8. Which one or more of the following physical quantities is directly dependent on
    electronegativity differences?
    (a) dipole moment   (b) electron affinity   (c) partial ionic bond character
    (d) bond energy   (e) bond length   (f) nucleophilic character

9. Write down approximate values for the Pauling electronegativities of the following
    elements: hydrogen, fluorine, caesium, nitrogen, manganese.

10. Which are generally the more electronegative, metals or non-metals?

11. Should the attack of NH_3 (ammonolysis) on BF_3 lead to the formation of the
    following bonds? (a) N–F and B–H or (b) B–N and H–F.

12. List the three elements which are most likely to form strong hydrogen bonds.

13. Which compound in each of the following series is predicted to be the most ionic?
    (a) $MgCl_2$, $AlCl_3$, PCl_3;   (b) CO_2, GeO_2, PbO_2.

PART 1

Electrons in Atoms

F5.1 Earlier programmes may be consulted for treatments of ionisation energy and electron affinity. We only summarise this material here.

(a) If an atom is supplied with sufficient energy, it will lose its most weakly bound electron, and become singly ionised.

$$A \rightarrow A^+ + e^-$$

The energy *absorbed* when one mole of gaseous atoms *loses* the outermost electron from each atom is referred to as its first *ionisation energy*, E_i.

(b) Correspondingly, an atom may add one electron,

$$A + e^- \rightarrow A^-$$

and in doing so, evolve energy and become more stable (as with the halogens). The energy *evolved* when one mole of gaseous atoms *gains* one electron on each atom is known as its *electron affinity*, E_a.

(Note that the above definition of electron affinity results in *positive* values if energy is *evolved* in adding an electron.)

Some texts use the opposite sign convention; these programmes consistently use the above definition.

(c) Ionisation energy increases from left to right across a period, and decreases from top to bottom of a group of the periodic table. There are a few irregularities in this overall trend.

(d) The variation of electron affinity is less regular. There is a tendency for electron affinity also to increase from left to right and to increase from top to bottom. (The addition of a second electron, as in forming O^{2-}, may make the evolution of energy negative for the total process of adding two electrons.)

(e) Tables of ionisation energies, electron affinities and electronegativities are provided at the end of the book (pp. 82–89) and also for convenience in appropriate positions in this programme.

Electrons in Molecules

We shall now see how the ideas of ionisation energy and electron affinity apply when the atoms concerned are incorporated into molecules.

F5.2 In the fluorine molecule, F_2, do the individual atoms differ in ionisation energy (E_i) or in electron affinity (E_a)? (*Both differ/neither differ/E_i's differ/E_a's differ.*)

A5.2 Neither differ.

F5.3 In that case, will there be an overall transfer of electrons from one to another?

A5.3 No.

Table of First Ionisation Energies (eV)

1 eV ≡ 96.5 kJ mol^{-1}

H 13.6																	He 24.6
Li 5.4	Be 9.3											B 8.4	C 11.3	N 14.6	O 13.6	F 17.4	Ne 21.7
Na 5.2	Mg 7.8											Al 6.0	Si 8.2	P 11.1	S 10.4	Cl 13.0	Ar 15.8
K 4.3	Ca 6.1	Sc 6.6	Ti 6.9	V 6.8	Cr 6.8	Mn 7.5	Fe 7.9	Co 7.9	Ni 7.7	Cu 7.8	Zn 9.4	Ga 6.0	Ge 7.9	As 9.9	Se 9.8	Br 11.9	Kr 14.1
Rb 4.2	Sr 5.7	Y 6.4	Zr 6.9	Nb 6.9	Mo 7.1	Tc 7.3	Ru 7.4	Rh 7.5	Pd 8.4	Ag 7.6	Cd 9.0	In 5.8	Sn 7.4	Sb 8.7	Te 9.1	I 10.5	Xe 12.1
Cs 3.9	Ba 5.3	La 5.6	Hf 7.0	Ta 7.9	W 8.0	Re 7.9	Os 8.7	Ir 9.1	Pt 9.1	Au 9.3	Hg 10.4	Tl 6.1	Pb 7.4	Bi 7.3	Po 8.4	At	Rn 10.8
Fr	Ra 5.3	Ac 7.0															

Ce 5.6	Pr 5.5	Nd 5.5	Pm	Sm 5.6	Eu 5.7	Gd 6.2	Tb 6.0	Dy	Ho	Er 6.1	Tm 5.8	Yb 6.2	Lu 6.2
Th 7.0	Pa	U 6.1	Np	Pu 5.8	Am 6.0								

Table of First Electron Affinities (eV)

(Addition of one electron)

$1\ eV \equiv 96.5\ kJ\ mol^{-1}$

H							
0.8							

Li	Be			B	C	N	O	F
0.5	−0.6			0.3	1.1	−0.3	1.5	3.5

Na	Mg			Al	Si	P	S	Cl
0.8	−0.3			0.5	1.4	0.8	2.1	3.7

K		Cu					Se	Br
0.7		1.5					2.2	3.4

		Ag					Te	I
		2.0					2.3	3.1

		Au	Hg					At
		2.8	1.5					2.6

F5.4 What about the HF molecule? Look up the electron affinities of the two atoms, note whether they differ and if so on which atom the electrons will tend to be concentrated in the molecules.

- -

A5.4 Fluorine has the numerically greater affinity and will therefore tend to attract more of the electrons in the molecule than will hydrogen.

F5.5 Also look up the first ionisation energies of the two atoms. Which loses an electron most easily? Does this lead to the same conclusion as above about the direction of electron transfer in HF? (*Yes/no.*)

- -

A5.5 Yes. Both approaches show that fluorine tends to attract electrons from hydrogen.

F5.6 In the same way consider HCl. What do the E_i's and E_a's each predict?

- -

A5.6 E_i's predict that hydrogen attracts more electrons than chlorine; but E_a's predict the reverse.

F5.7 If we try to measure the *electron attracting ability* of chlorine in HCl, we therefore expect it to result from a compromise between which two quantities?

- -

A5.7 Ionisation energies and electron affinities. Here the latter is decisive.

F5.8 A knowledge of ionisation energies and electron affinities therefore allows us to define a third quantity relating to an atom in a molecule. What is this quantity?

_ _

    A5.8 Electron attracting ability.

F5.9 We call this electron attracting power of an atom in a molecule its **electronegativity**, since the atom doing the attracting of electrons will tend to gain a charge. What sign has this charge?

_ _

    A5.9 Negative.

F5.10 In that case, is fluorine more or less electronegative than hydrogen?

_ _

    A5.10 Fluorine is more electronegative than hydrogen.

F5.11 And is chlorine more electronegative than hydrogen?

_ _

    A5.11 Yes.

We shall see later that electronegativity has important consequences in determining types of bonds and chemical reactions. So let us return to the problem of measuring it.

Mulliken's Approach

F5.12 Mulliken considered the energies involved in the formation of gaseous X^+Y^- and X^-Y^+ from gaseous atoms X and Y. Writing the ionisation energies as $E_i(X)$ and $E_i(Y)$ and the electron affinities as $E_a(X)$ and $E_a(Y)$, the energies *absorbed* are respectively _____ and _____ . (Remember the way electron affinity is defined and try to use the correct signs.)

_ _

    A5.12 $E_i(X) - E_a(Y)$ and $E_i(Y) - E_a(X)$.

F5.13 If Y is more electronegative than X, then which will be formed more easily, X^+Y^- or X^-Y^+?

_ _

    A5.13 X^+Y^-.

F5.14 Therefore the energies absorbed (see **F5.12**) are in the order _____ <

_____ .

_ _

    A5.14 $E_i(X) - E_a(Y) < E_i(Y) - E_a(X)$.

F5.15 Rearrange this with all the X quantities on the left and all the Y quantities on the right as _____ < _____ .

A5.15 $E_i(X) + E_a(X) < E_i(Y) + E_a(Y)$.

F5.16 Is the quantity $(E_i + E_a)$ greater for the more electronegative element or for the less electronegative element?

A5.16 For the more electronegative element.

F5.17 Mulliken therefore used this quantity, actually $(E_i + E_a)/2$, as a measure of the electronegativity of an atom.

F5.18 Use the tables of electron affinities and first ionisation energies (pp. 50–51) to construct a table of Mulliken's electronegativity. Fill in the value (in eV), where available, under the appropriate atom in the table below.

H							
Li	Be		B	C	N	O	F
Na	Mg		Al	Si	P	S	Cl
K		Cu				Se	Br
		Ag					
		Au	Hg				

Note: It is not important that you calculate all these values.

A5.18 Table of Mulliken Electronegativities (eV)

H							
7.2							
Li	Be		B	C	N	O	F
3.0	4.4		4.4	6.2	7.2	7.6	10.5
Na	Mg		Al	Si	P	S	Cl
3.0	3.8		3.3	4.8	6.0	6.3	8.4
K		Cu				Se	Br
2.5		4.7				6.0	7.7
		Ag				Te	I
		4.8				5.7	6.8
		Au	Hg				
		6.1	6.0				

Note that the table is incomplete, due to lack of data on electron affinities.

F5.19 This is the main difficulty with Mulliken's approach. A further difficulty is that the ionisation energies and electron affinities apply to the atoms in one state. Which state (*solid/liquid/gaseous*) is this?

A5.19 Gaseous.

F5.20 In a molecule, the atoms are not isolated as they are in a gas, and further they may be in a valence state rather than in the ground state.

F5.21 Explain the difference between the definitions of electron affinity and electronegativity, both of which refer to the ability of an atom to attract electrons.

A5.21 Electron affinity refers to an isolated gaseous atom, whereas electronegativity refers to an atom bound in a molecule.

F5.22 This effect of neighbouring atoms on the electron-attracting power of an atom is emphasised by an examination of your tables of E_i's, E_a's and electronegativities. Which quantity (E_i or E_a) usually dominates the electronegativity?

A5.22 Ionisation energy, since it is numerically larger than electron affinity.

F5.23 Thus the trends in electronegativity usually follow those of which quantity?

A5.23 Ionisation energy—actually the *first* ionisation energy.

F5.24 So will the electronegativity usually increase or decrease in going from left to right in a row of the periodic table?

A5.24 Increase.

F5.25 And will it increase or decrease in going down a group of the periodic table?

A5.25 Decrease.

F5.26 Therefore, for example, is selenium more or less electronegative than germanium? Is beryllium more or less electronegative than barium?

A5.26 More; more.

F5.27 If we move diagonally, for example from Be to Al, would we expect the electronegativity to increase, decrease or remain about the same?

A5.27 Remain about the same. This is the 'diagonal relationship'.

Summary of Part 1

(a) Within a covalent molecule some atoms have a greater tendency to attract the shared electrons than others. This electron-attracting power of an atom in a molecule is known as its electronegativity.

(b) Electronegativity is related to electron affinity but is distinguished from it in that the latter quantity refers to isolated gaseous atoms.

(c) Mulliken derived a scale of electronegativity in which it is related to the first ionisation energy and the electron affinity.

(d) The periodic variation of electronegativity follows that of first ionisation energy.

PART 2

Ensure that you are familiar with the summary of Part 1 before proceeding.

F5.28 Let us return to the subject of scales of electronegativity. The first we have discussed already, and was due to Mulliken, who related electronegativity to which quantities?

A5.28 Ionisation energy and electron affinity.

Pauling's Approach

F5.29 In HF the negative charge is attracted to one atom, resulting in a partial separation of charge within the molecule. These partial charges may be represented as $\delta+$ and $\delta-$, and we indicate them on the diagram of the molecule as

$$H-F$$

Complete this diagram by inserting the correct signs.

A5.29 $H^{\delta+}-F^{\delta-}$.

F5.30 There are two poles of opposite charge, a so-called **dipole**, whose magnitude is measured by the charge multiplied by the distance between the charges (the bond length, r). This **dipole moment**, μ, is therefore given by the expression $\mu = $ _____ .

A5.30 $\mu = \delta \times r$.

F5.31 These dipole moments have important consequences when we consider interactions between molecules, but for the moment we are interested in the partial **ionic** character which they confer on the molecule. We are saying that HF behaves as if it were partially the ionic molecule H^+F^-, unlike some compounds which are almost purely ionic, and other molecules which are purely covalent. Give some examples of very ionic and of purely covalent molecules.

_ _

A5.31 Ionic: Na^+Cl^-; K^+F^-, $Ca^{2+}O^{2-}$, etc.; covalent: Cl_2, H_2, O_3, P_4, etc.

F5.32 Pauling saw that this electrostatic attraction between the two atoms in HF due to partial ionic character would affect the bond strength. Would the bond be weakened or strengthed?

_ _

A5.32 Strengthened.

F5.33 Is the measured bond energy D_{AB} of a molecule AB greater than or less than the mean bond energy of the two molecules A_2 and B_2? This effect Pauling related to a difference between atoms A and B in terms of which quantity?

_ _

A5.33 Greater; electronegativity.

F5.34 This extra bond energy Δ_{AB} is given in terms of D_{AB}, D_{A_2} and D_{B_2} by _____.

_ _

A5.34 $\Delta_{AB} = D_{AB} - \frac{1}{2}(D_{A_2} + D_{B_2})$.

F5.35 Pauling found that a linear scale of electronegativity (x) could be constructed if he related differences in this quantity to Δ_{AB} in the following way:

$$(x_A - x_B) = \sqrt{(\Delta_{AB}/23.06)}$$

(23.06 is a factor for converting kilocalories, the common units for bond energy, to electron volts, the usual units for x, E_i and E_a.)

However this does not give absolute electronegativities. What does it give?

_ _

A5.35 Differences in electronegativities.

F5.36 To get a proper scale of electronegativity, Pauling arbitrarily fixed the value for hydrogen as $x_H = 2.1$. Calculate the electronegativity for fluorine, and for caesium, from the following information:

$D_{HF} = 135$; $D_{H_2} = 104$; $D_{F_2} = 38$; $D_{CsF} = 125$; $D_{Cs_2} = 11$; all in kcal mol^{-1}.

_ _

A5.36 $x_F = 3.8$; $x_{Cs} = 1.7$. If you got these wrong it is probably because you looked them up rather than working them out. One of the failings of Pauling's approach is that the values are not exactly additive. Pauling selected values which were more self-consistent. He took $x_{Cs} = 0.8$ and $x_F = 4.0$.

F5.37 From what we have already seen, which element should be the most electronegative and which should be the least electronegative of the natural elements?

_ _

A5.37 Fluorine most; caesium least.

F5.38 Generally are non-metals very electronegative or not? Metals are opposite and
we may anticipate that they are referred to as being very electro_____ .

A5.38 Very electronegative; electropositive.

F5.39 There are other scales of electronegativity, such as that due to Allred and
Rochow, which is based on the force of attraction between a nucleus and the electrons
at the outside of the atom. The scales we have discussed are due to Mulliken and
Pauling and relate electronegativities to which quantities?

A5.39 Mulliken: ionisation energies and electron affinities; Pauling: bond
energies.

F5.40 The table on p. 58 gives Pauling electronegativities. Compare these with the
Mulliken values given earlier (F5.18). Plot accurately, on graph paper, the available
Mulliken electronegativities against corresponding Pauling values for the same atom.
There is a rough relationship between the two scales: Mulliken electronegativity/Pauling
electronegativity =_____ .

A5.40 About 3.1.

Summary of Part 2
(a) When a molecule contains atoms of differing electronegativity, the unequal
distribution of electrons will create partial ionic charges and hence a permanent
dipole moment.
(b) Pauling's scale of electronegativity is linearly related to Mulliken's and is based on
the extra bond strength derived from partial ionic character.
(c) Allred and Rochow defined a scale of electronegativity based on the force each
atom exerts on the shared electrons.
(d) Non-metals are more electronegative than metals.

PART 3

Ensure that you understand the points covered in the summary of Part 2 before
proceeding.

Application of the Electronegativity Concept
(a) Dipole moments
F5.41 Use a table of the Pauling values of the electronegativities of the elements to
determine which way round the dipole is ($A^{\delta+}B^{\delta-}$ or $A^{\delta-}B^{\delta+}$) in the following diatomic
molecules: HI, CO, ClF, ICl.

Table of Pauling Electronegativities
(Figures in parentheses are estimated values)

1	2	3	4	5	6	7	8	9	10	11	12	13	14	15	16	17
H 2.1																
Li 1.0	Be 1.6											B 2.0	C 2.6	N 3.0	O 3.4	F 4.0
Na 0.9	Mg 1.3											Al 1.6	Si 1.9	P 2.2	S 2.6	Cl 3.2
K 0.8	Ca 1.0	Sc 1.4	Ti 1.5	V 1.6	Cr 1.7	Mn 1.6	Fe 1.8	Co 1.9	Ni 1.9	Cu 1.9	Zn 1.7	Ga 1.8	Ge 2.0	As 2.2	Se 2.6	Br 3.0
Rb 0.8	Sr 1.0	Y 1.2	Zr 1.3	Nb (1.6)	Mo 2.2	Tc (1.9)	Ru (2.2)	Rh 2.3	Pd 2.2	Ag 1.9	Cd 1.7	In 1.8	Sn 2.0	Sb 2.0	Te (2.4)	I 2.7
Cs 0.8	Ba 0.9	La (1.1)	Hf (1.3)	Ta (1.5)	W 2.4	Re (1.9)	Os (2.2)	Ir 2.2	Pt 2.3	Au 2.5	Hg 2.0	Tl 2.0	Pb 2.3	Bi 2.0	Po (2.0)	At (2.2)
		Ac (1.1)														

Ce (1.1)	Pr (1.1)	Nd (1.1)	Pm (1.1)	Sm (1.1)	Eu (1.1)	Gd (1.1)	Tb (1.2)	Dy (1.2)	Ho (1.2)	Er (1.2)	Tm (1.2)	Yb (1.2)	Lu (1.2)
Th (1.3)	Pa (1.5)	U (1.4)	Np (1.3)	Pu (1.3)									

A5.41 $H^{\delta+}I^{\delta-}$; $C^{\delta+}O^{\delta-}$; $Cl^{\delta+}F^{\delta-}$; $I^{\delta+}Cl^{\delta-}$.

F5.42 The electronegativity difference on the Pauling scale is approximately equal to the dipole moment (in Debye units, D). What is the approximate dipole moment of HBr?

N.B. One Debye is the dipole moment of two opposite charges of 10^{-10} e.s.u. separated by a distance of 1Å. In SI units, $D = 3.34 \times 10^{-30}$ C m.

A5.42 0.9 D; the observed value is 0.8 D.

(b) Hydrolysis mechanisms

F5.43 Consider the relative electronegativities of the atoms in Cl_2O. Which atoms will have a partial negative charge and which will have a partial positive charge?

A5.43 Negative: oxygen; positive: chlorine.
Thus:

$$\delta- O \Big\langle {}^{Cl^{\delta+}}_{Cl^{\delta+}}$$

F5.44 So for the whole Cl_2O molecule the oxygen atom is partially negatively charged while each chlorine atom has a partial positive charge. At which atom(s) would a reagent attack Cl_2O if it was seeking negative charge (an electrophilic reagent)?

A5.44 Oxygen.

F5.45 Such a reagent is water when attacking through which atom(s)?
Hint: use the electronegativity of H and O to write partial charges on the structure of H_2O.

A5.45 Hydrogen.

F5.46 This reaction would lead to the formation of O–H bonds, each Cl atom being lost as HOCl. What would be the final product(s) of the hydrolysis of Cl_2O?

A5.46 HOCl (and H_2O).

F5.47 Will BCl_3 hydrolyse in the same way? Justify your answer.

A5.47 No, because boron is less electronegative than chlorine and therefore will bear a partial positive charge, while the chlorine atoms each have a partial negative charge. The boron atom is no longer suitable for attack by an electro-philic reagent.

F5.48 It is suitable, however, for attack by a reagent looking for positive 'nuclei' (a nucleophilic reagent), such as water when attacking through which atom(s)?

- -

A5.48 Oxygen.

F5.49 What type of bonds (B–H/B–O/Cl–O) will therefore be formed?

- -

A5.49 B–O.

F5.50 Chlorine atoms are removed as HCl, being replaced by hydroxyl groups, the final products being _____ .

- -

A5.50 HCl and $B(OH)_3$, i.e. H_3BO_3.

F5.51 Thus we see how electronegativity may affect reactions. Likewise, the first member of a periodic group often differs from the second member in such ways because of its electronegativity. Does the first member have a greater or a smaller electronegativity than the second member?

- -

A5.51 Greater.

(c) Hydrogen bonding
F5.52 There are other factors involved also, such as the availability of d orbitals for bond formation with the second members in a periodic group, and the importance of hydrogen bond formation for the first member. It is found that hydrogen forms rather weak secondary bonds to the most electronegative elements. List the four elements which are most likely to form such **hydrogen bonds**.

- -

A5.52 F, O, N and Cl.

F5.53 There are other factors involved in hydrogen bonding, such as the presence of non-bonding electrons, but we shall concentrate on the electronegativity factor. Which of the following molecules is most likely to form hydrogen bonds from, for example, water, to the central atom: Cl_2O; BCl_3; PCl_3?

- -

A5.53 Cl_2O.

F5.54 These weak O-----H bonds in fact form the path for the hydrolysis of Cl_2O mentioned above. A further aspect of hydrogen bonds is that work must be done to break them when a liquid or solid containing them is vaporised. Which of each of the following pairs of hydrides will therefore have the higher boiling point? NH_3 or PH_3; H_2O or H_2S; HF or HCl.

_____

A5.54 NH_3; H_2O; HF.

_____

F5.55 These boiling points are anomalously high due to hydrogen bonding with which atoms?

_____

A5.55 N, O and F.

_____

(d) Ionic character
F5.56 Let us turn to one last effect of electronegativity. Which of the following molecules will have the most, and which the least, partial ionic character? BN, Na_2O, $TeCl_4$, IBr, ZnH_2.

_____

A5.56 Most, Na_2O; least, IBr.

_____

F5.57 Expressions have been proposed for percentage ionic character but we shall use the concept only qualitatively. However, we may say that Na_2O is the most ionic of these compounds and IBr is the least ionic, i.e. the most covalent. We may expect a molecule in which the bonding is purely covalent when the electronegativity difference has what value?
Give some examples of such molecules.

_____

A5.57 Zero. Any homonuclear molecule such as Cl_2, P_4, S_8.

_____

F5.58 Strictly we never get a purely ionic molecule, but which compound will come nearest?

_____

A5.58 CsF.

_____

F5.59 We shall see later that the extents of ionic or covalent character have important consequences in determining types of structure and reactions.

_____

Now repeat the programme test on p. 48, and mark it as before. If you score greater than 27 you have successfully completed this programme.

_____

Summary

1. Within a covalent molecule some atoms have a greater tendency to attract the shared electrons than others. This electron attracting power of an atom in a molecule is known as its electronegativity.

2. Electronegativity is related to electron affinity but is distinguished from it in that the latter quantity refers to isolated atoms in the gaseous state.

3. Mulliken derived a scale of electronegativity in which it is related to the first ionisation energy and the electron affinity.

4. When a molecule contains atoms of differing electronegativity, the unequal distribution of electrons will create partial ionic charges and hence a permanent dipole moment.

5. Pauling's scale of electronegativity is linearly related to Mulliken's and is based on the extra bond strength derived from partial ionic character.

6. Allred and Rochow defined a scale of electronegativity based on the force an atom exerts on a (shared) electron at the outside of the atom.

7. The periodic variation of electronegativity follows that of first ionisation energy. Hence, non-metals are more electronegative than metals.

8. The greater the electronegativity difference between the atoms in a molecule, the greater will be the ionic character of the bond.

9. Electrophiles will attack the most negative atom, and nucleophiles the most positive atom within a molecule.

10. The very electronegative atoms nitrogen, oxygen and fluorine are often involved in hydrogen bonding.

Chapter **6**

Polarisation and Polarisability

Mr. B.O. Field

City University, London EC1V 4PB

Introduction

Chemical compounds are formed by electrons of the atoms in the compound interacting with each other.

On a purely ionic bond model, A^+B^-, the charge separation is assumed to be complete. On a model where the bonding is 100% covalent the electrons forming the bond A–B are shared exactly between atom A and atom B.

We find, in real compounds, the 100% ionic or 100% covalent almost never occurs and in this programme we are going to explore some of the factors which influence the sharing of electrons between atoms of elements and some of the physico-chemical consequences of this sharing.

Our goal is to be able to predict the relative contribution of ionic and covalent bonding in a series of molecules, to predict their relative melting points and solubilities and to be able to say something about why certain elements in different periodic groups have similar chemistries.

Objectives

When you have completed this programme you should be able to:

1. Predict the relative sizes of neutral atoms, their cations and anions.

2. Predict the relative polarising power of ions.

3. Predict which species are more susceptible to polarisation.

4. Predict the relative ionic contribution to a series of similar chemical bonds.

5. Estimate the effect of nuclear charge on the polarising power of a given cation.

6. Predict the relative solubilities of salts.

7. Estimate the relative melting points of a series of related compounds.

8. Illustrate the qualitative link between polarisability and electronegativity.

9. Account for the diagonal relationships in the periodic table.

10. Illustrate the danger of using polarisation concepts in isolation from other physico-chemical evidence.

Programme Test

Before starting the programme itself, try the following test. Answers and scores are on p. 94. If you score greater than 12 you do not need to study the programme. .

1. Which species in each of the following sets has the largest radius?
    (a) I, I^+, I^-;   (b) Fe^{2+}, Fe^{3+}.

2. Which will have the greater polarising power, Fe^{3+} or Fe^{2+}?

3. Which of the following species will be most susceptible to polarisation effects, Cl^+, Cl or Cl^-?

4. Which of each of the following pairs of bonds contains the larger ionic contribution to the bonding?
    (a) $K-F$ or $K-I$;   (b) $Fe^{2+}-X$ or $Fe^{3+}-X$.

5. Which would you predict is the more powerful polariser, Cu^+ or Na^+, given that they have similar radii?

6. Would you predict that LiCl or KCl has the higher solubility in alcohol?

7. List the halides of Ca in order of increasing melting points.

8. List the halogen atoms in order of increasing (a) polarisability and (b) electro-negativity.

9. Explain why the chemistries of (a) Li and Mg; (b) Be and Al; and (c) B and Si show such close similarities.

10. (a) List the chlorides of Na^+, K^+ and Rb^+ in the expected order of increasing covalent contributions to the metal-chlorine bond, using polarisation concepts only.

    (b) Now place these chlorides in the order you would expect their melting points to increase on the above basis.

    (c) The actual melting points are RbCl, $715°C$; KCl, $776°C$; and NaCl, $800°C$. Why is this?

F6.1 When an atom loses an electron to form a cation, M^+, the size decreases due to the electrons remaining in the ionic form experiencing a greater attractive pull from the the nuclear protons.

Na^+ is *larger/smaller* than Na due to the *greater/smaller* attractive force on the electrons by the nucleus.

- -

      A6.1 Smaller, greater.

F6.2 If an atom can lose more than one electron to produce a divalent cation M^{2+}, or a trivalent cation M^{3+}, etc., then the cationic radius decreases with an increase in the electrostatic charge. Hence M^{3+} is smaller than M^{2+} because there are *less/more* electrons in M^{3+} to counteract the attractive pull of the nuclear protons.

- -

      A6.2 Less.

F6.3 Place the following ions in order of increasing size: M^{2+}, M^+, M^{3+}.

———————————————————————————————————————

A6.3 $M^{3+} < M^{2+} < M^+$.

F6.4 If an atom gains an electron and forms an anion, A^-, then the size of the anion will be greater than that of the neutral atom as the nuclear protons will now have less attractive pull per electron in the anion. Hence I is *larger/smaller* than I^- because of the *greater/less* attractive nuclear force experienced by its electrons.

———————————————————————————————————————

A6.4 Smaller, greater.

F6.5 Place the following species in order of decreasing size: (a) I^+, I^-, I; (b) Fe, Fe^{3+}, Fe^{2+}.

———————————————————————————————————————

A6.5 $I^- > I > I^+$; $Fe > Fe^{2+} > Fe^{3+}$.

F6.6 Since the electrons in a cation are more strongly held than those in an anion, they will be less susceptible to electrostatic influence tending to distort them from spherical symmetry. The more strongly held the electrons, the less susceptible to electrostatic distortion, i.e. polarisation, will be the ion, and vice versa. Therefore I^- will be *less/more* susceptible to polarisation than I, and I^+ will be *less/more* susceptible to polarisation than I^-.

———————————————————————————————————————

A6.6 More, less.

F6.7 In general the electrons in a cation are so strongly held that we do not need to consider any electrostatic distortion or polarisation of the electron cloud. In a cation the electrons are so *compact/diffuse* that we need not consider polarisation effects.

———————————————————————————————————————

A6.7 Compact.

F6.8 Electrons in an anion on the other hand are very diffuse as the nuclear attraction has been reduced on the formation of the anion and hence the electrons in an anion are are highly susceptible to polarisation effects.
Hence anions are much *smaller/larger* than cations and therefore they are *less/more* susceptible to polarisation.

———————————————————————————————————————

A6.8 Larger, more.

F6.9 For a given element, the larger the anion the *less/more* negative charge it carries, and the *less/more* susceptible it will be towards polarisation.

———————————————————————————————————————

A6.9 More, more.

F6.10 A^{2-} will be *less/more* susceptible to polarisation than A^-.

A6.10 More.

F6.11 In an ionic compound A^+B^- the compact electron cloud of the cation A^+ will not be significantly influenced by the presence of B^-. However, the electrons of the anion B^-, being so diffuse and weakly held, will be polarised by the electrostatic field produced by A^+.

Hence, Na^+ *will/will not* be polarised by the presence of Cl^- in Na^+Cl^- and Cl^- *will/will not* be polarised by the presence of Na^+ in Na^+Cl^-.

A6.11 Will not; will.

F6.12 In Li^+I^- the polarising power of the small Li^+ cation will polarise the electrons of the electronically diffuse large I^- anion *towards/away from* the cation.

A6.12 Towards.

F6.13 The displacement of electron density from the anion towards the cation due to the polarising power of the small positive ion on the large diffuse negative ion decreases the electrostatic charge separation and hence decreases the degree of ionic bonding in the compound. This may be seen in the diagram below.

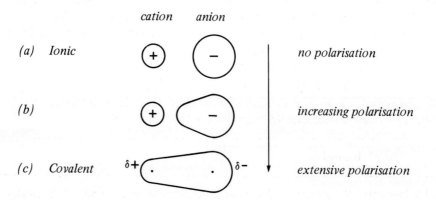

Therefore we would expect that Li^+I^- would be *more/less* ionic than Li^+F^-, and Li^+F^- would be *more/less* ionic than Cs^+F^-.

A6.13 Less. less.

F6.14 The smaller the cation and the more positive charge it carries, the greater is its polarising effect on a given anion.

Place the following bonds in order of decreasing ionic character: M^+-Cl^-, $M^{3+}-Cl^-$, $M^{2+}-Cl^-$.

A6.14 $M^+-Cl^- > M^{2+}-Cl^- > M^{3+}-Cl^-$.

F6.15 Place the alkali metal bromides in increasing order of ionic character.

A6.15 $LiBr < NaBr < KBr < RbBr < CsBr$.

F6.16 Polarising power depends not only on electrostatic charge and ion size but also on the electronic configuration of the ion, as this will determine how effectively the electrons can screen the nuclear charge. For example, Na^+ has the configuration $1s^2 2s^2 2p^6$ and an ionic radius of 1.0Å; Cu^+ has the configuration $1s^2 2s^2 2p^6 3s^2 3p^6 3d^{10}$ and a radius of 1.0Å. In spite of their ionic radii being similar, Cu^+ has a greater polarising power than Na^+ as the d electrons in Cu^+ have a poor screening effect on the nuclear charge and hence the positive nuclear core is more exposed in Cu^+; this gives Cu^+ greater polarising power compared to Na^+, which has no d electrons in its electronic structure.

Which bond would you expect to be more covalent, Na^+-Cl^- or Cu^+-Cl^-?
Which bond would you expect to be more covalent, $Ca^{2+}-Cl^-$ or $Cd^{2+}-Cl^-$?

A6.16 Cu^+-Cl^-; $Cd^{2+}-Cl^-$.

F6.17 Values of lattice energies, U, for 18-electron cations often exhibit deviations from those predicted by thermodynamic cycles based on a pure ionic model.

The differences between U(experimental) and U(calculated) for the following salts are:

RbI	$\Delta = 17$ kJ mol^{-1};
CdI$_2$	$\Delta = 361$ kJ mol^{-1};
PbO$_2$	$\Delta = 890$ kJ mol^{-1}.

This increasing deviation from the predicted lattice energy is due to an *increasing/ decreasing* deviation from ideal ionic character in these compounds.

A6.17 Increasing.

F6.18 In general, the greater the degree of ionic character in a compound the greater will be its solubility in polar solvents like water.

Place the compounds RbI, CdI$_2$, PbO$_2$ in order of increasing solubility in water.

A6.18 $PbO_2 < CdI_2 < RbI$.

F6.19 The transition from ionic to covalent bonding is often accompanied by reductions in electrical conductivities of aqueous solutions, in melting points, and in solubility in polar solvents.

Which would you expect to have the lower melting point, NaCl or CuCl?

A6.19 CuCl, m.p. 422°C. (NaCl , m.p. 800°C.)

F6.20 As we have seen in **F6.8**, the larger the anion the more susceptible it is to polarisation.

Place the halides of Ca in order of (a) increasing ionic character; (b) decreasing melting points.

A6.20 (a) $CaI_2 < CaBr_2 < CaCl_2 < CaF_2$;
(b) CaF_2 (1382°C) > $CaCl_2$ (772°C) > $CaBr_2$ (730°C) > CaI_2 (575°C).

F6.21 As we have seen in **F6.2**, increasing electrostatic charge on a cation decreases its size and so increases its polarising power.

The following ions have the radii given: Ca^{2+}, 1.0Å; Mg^{2+}, 0.7Å; Al^{3+}, 0.5Å; Na^+, 1.0Å. Place their chlorides in order of (a) decreasing covalent character; (b) increasing melting point.

A6.21 (a) $AlCl_3 > MgCl_2 > CaCl_2 > NaCl$;
(b) $AlCl_3$ (193°C, in a sealed tube) < $MgCl_2$ (712°C) < $CaCl_2$ (772°C) < NaCl (800°C).

F6.22 It is found that first row elements, especially Li, Be and B, have certain chemical resemblances to the second member of the following group, This is often referred to as the diagonal relationship.

Li   Be   B   C
Na   Mg   Al   Si

LiCl is appreciably soluble in ethyl alcohol as is $MgCl_2$, but the other group I chlorides are almost insoluble in this solvent. $BeCl_2$ and $AlCl_3$ are both volatile solids with a dimeric bridge structure in the vapour phase, whereas the other chlorides of group II metals melt at a high temperature. It is suggested that the *large/small* ionic radius of the first row elements endows them with a particularly *small/large* polarising power which accounts for the particularly *high/low* contributions of covalency to the bonding. Thus they are comparable with a more highly-charged (but larger) cation in the next group.

A6.22 Small, large, high;

F6.23 The concept of polarisation arose out of the work of Karl Fajans in 1924. It has largely been replaced by the more quantitative concept of electronegativity which is defined by Pauling as the tendency of an atom in a molecule to attract the bonding electrons to itself. Hence we see that the larger the electronegativity difference across a chemical bond, the greater will be the ionic contributions to the bonding. We have seen (F5.23) that electronegativity values usually follow the first ionisation energy which in turn is dependent upon electronic configuration and size of the atom or ion; and it is here that we have the link with the concept of polarisation. In general, for a related group of elements, the smaller the atom size the larger is the electronegativity value and the lower the polarisability.

Place the halogen atoms in order of (a) increasing electronegativity; (b) increasing polarisability; (c) increasing first ionisation energy.

--- --- --- --- --- --- --- --- --- --- --- --- --- --- --- --- --- --- ---

A6.23 I (2.7) < Br (3.0) < Cl (3.2) < F (4.0) (Pauling values); (b) F < Cl < Br < I; (c) I (1020) < Br (1150) < Cl (1250) < F (1680) (kJ mol^{-1}).

F6.24 Now refer back to **F6.19**. The electronegativity of Ca on the Pauling scale is 1.0. Using the halogen electronegativities given above, calculate the electronegativity difference across the calcium-halogen bond and hence again place the calcium halides in order of increasing ionic character.

--- --- --- --- --- --- --- --- --- --- --- --- --- --- --- --- --- --- ---

A6.24 Δ(electronegativity) CaI_2 (1.7) < $CaBr_2$ (2.0) < $CaCl_2$ (2.2) < CaF_2 (3.0). This is the same order as that deduced on grounds of the relative polarisability of the halogen atoms.

F6.25 A word of warning about the indiscriminate application of polarisation ideas is needed. It is manifestly impossible to divorce one factor from all others in every case as we have largely done here: this can lead us to incorrect predictions.

Place the chlorides of Na^+, K^+, Rb^+ in the expected order of decreasing covalent contributions to the bonding using only polarisation concepts.

--- --- --- --- --- --- --- --- --- --- --- --- --- --- --- --- --- --- ---

A6.25 Na^+Cl^- > K^+Cl^- > Rb^+Cl^-.

F6.26 Now place these chlorides in the order of increasing melting points expected on these grounds.

--- --- --- --- --- --- --- --- --- --- --- --- --- --- --- --- --- --- ---

A6.26 NaCl < KCl < RbCl; but the melting points do not substantiate this: NaCl, 800°C, KCl, 776°C, RbCl, 715°C.

F6.27 We have seen in **F6.25** and **F6.26** that the use of polarisation ideas in isolation from other physical parameters such as the lattice energy has led us to an incorrect order of melting points in this case. The lattice energy of NaCl is 775 kJ mol^{-1} whilst that of KCl is 702 kJ mol^{-1}.

Nevertheless the concept of polarisation is useful in making approximate comparisons between the properties of molecules and we shall employ it in conjunction with other concepts in the programmes relating to the chemistry of the elements.

Now repeat the programme test on p. 64, and mark it as before. If you score greater than 12 you have successfully completed the programme.

Summary

1. The electron cloud of an atom or ion is susceptible to distortion by electrostatic interaction caused by a neighbouring cation or anion. This effect is known as **polarisation**.

2. Since the electrons in a cation are more strongly held than those in an anion, they will be less susceptible to electrostatic influences tending to distort them from spherical symmetry. Thus anions tend to be more polarisable than cations.

3. In a cation the electrons are so compact that we need not consider polarisation effects. Electrons in an anion, on the other hand, are diffuse and the electrons are susceptible to polarisation. Thus anions tend to be **polarised** and cations tend to be the perturbing electrostatic charges, i.e. the **polarisers**.

4. For a given element, the larger the anion and the more negative charge it carries, the more **polarisable** it will be. The smaller the cation and the more positive charge it carries, the greater will be its polarising effects.

5. The displacement of electron density from the anion towards the cation, due to the **polarising power** of the small positive ion on the large diffuse negative ion, decreases the electrostatic charge separations and hence decreases the degree of ionic bonding in a compound. Thus, covalent bonding will be extensive when there is substantial polarisation, i.e. when large and highly negative anions are polarised by small and highly charged cations.

6. Polarising power depends not only on electrostatic charge and ion size but also on the electrostatic configuration of the ion, as this will determine how effectively the electrons can screen the nuclear charge. Thus, d electrons have a poor screening effect, and transition metal cations will have a greater polarising power than cations of a similar size with noble gas configurations.

7. High degrees of polarisation imply extensive covalent bond character which in turn is associated with low solubility in polar solvents, low electrical conductivity of aqueous colutions, low melting points, and increasing deviations from predicted lattice energies.

8. First row elements (Li, Be, B) have certain chemical resemblances to the second member of the following group (Mg, Al, Si). This is often called the "diagonal relationship", and may be explained in terms of the similar polarising power of the cations which yield similar degrees of covalent bond character.

9. In general, the smaller the atom size, the larger is the electronegativity value and the smaller the polarisability. The concepts of electronegativity and polarisability are related, and both may be used to understand the nature of bond types in particular compounds.

10. The use of polarisation ideas in isolation from other physical parameters, such as the lattice energy, may lead to incorrect predictions (for example, of melting points).

Chapter 7

Bond Types in Simple Inorganic Compounds

Professor B.J.Aylett

Westfield College, University of London, London NW3 7ST

Introduction

This programme shows how various concepts such as electronegativity, polarising power, polarisability, ionisation energy, coordination number and ion size may be used to infer the types of bonds present in a range of compounds AB_n ($n = 1-6$). The structures adopted by these compounds in the solid state are related in a general way to the nature of the bonds involved.

Prior Knowledge

This programme is the last in a set of six; earlier programmes have dealt with the concepts outlined above. The programme can be used in conjunction with a set of lectures, or for revision. The tables of data in Chapter 8 will be needed.

Objectives

When you have completed the programme you should be able to:

1. Explain the relationship between electronegativity differences and ionic character of bonds in binary compounds AB.

2. Explain the relation between polarising power and polarisability of ions, and ionic character of bonds in binary compounds.

3. Predict the bond types in various AB compounds, given values of electro-negativity and ionic radii.

4. Show the effect on bond type when AB adopts an extended 2- or 3-dimensional structure, i.e. the coordination numbers of A and B increase.

5. Describe the effect on bond types of AB_n compounds when n increases.

6. Predict the bond types in given AB_n compounds.

7. Recognise the occurrence of clusters of B atoms in AB_n compounds.

Programme Test

Before starting the programme itself, try the following test. Answers and scores are on p. 94. If you score greater than 16 you do not need to study the programme.

1. If the compound AB is ionic, what can you infer about the size of $(x_A - x_B)$, the difference in electronegativity between A and B?

2. What kind of bond will be formed between elements A and B of similar electronegativity?

3. The ions A^+, B^-, C^{2+}, D^{2-} all have the same radius. Is the compound AB more or less covalent than CD?

4. The ion A^+ is smaller than C^+, while B^- is larger than D^-. Is the compound AB more or less covalent than CD?

5. Given the values of electronegativity and ionic radii in the tables in Chapter 8, predict the bond types in the following compounds.
    (a) CsBr   (b) CuTe   (c) AlP   (d) NaHg   (e) ClF

6. What difference is there in predicted bond type between a diatomic molecule AB and a 3-dimensional structure with the same atoms each 6-coordinated by the other?

7. In passing along the series: RbF, SrF_2, YF_3, ZrF_4, NbF_5, MoF_6, do the compounds become more ionic or more covalent?

8. Predict the bond types in the following compounds.
    (a) AlI_3 (b) ThO_2 (c) $MgZn_2$ (d) OsO_4

9. Which of the following compounds are likely to contain clusters of atoms?
    (a) AgN_3 (b) WCl_6 (c) CrO_5 (d) K_2S_6

Bond Type: Resulting Compound Type

Armed with the concepts developed in the preceding programmes, we can now examine a wide range of bond types in binary compounds.

F7.1 In a compound AB, if A and B are of similar electronegativity, the bond will be essentially *ionic/covalent*.

- -

A7.1 Covalent.

F7.2 If B is much more electronegative than A, the bond will be essentially *metallic/ ionic/dative/covalent*.

- -

A7.2 Ionic.

F7.3 And electron density will be concentrated *around A/around B/between A and B*.

- -

A7.3 Around B (although A will also have an approximately spherical shell of non-bonding electrons unless it is hydrogen).

F7.4 It is often useful to consider intermediate cases in terms of the effect that an ion A^{m+} has on an ion of opposite charge B^{n-}. This effect is called *hybridisation/ polarisation/delocalisation*.

- -

- -

A7.4 Polarisation.

F7.5 It is most significant if the cation is *large/small.*

- -

A7.5 Small.

F7.6 And carries a *low/high* positive charge.

- -

A7.6 High.

F7.7 Similarly the anion is most readily polarised if its size is _____ and its charge is _____ .

- -

A7.7 Large, high.

F7.8 If such polarisation occurs, this is equivalent to saying the bond *has some covalent character/decreases in energy/increases in length.*

- -

A7.8 Has some covalent character. The actual (polarised) ionic bond will be shorter and of higher energy than a hypothetical purely ionic bond.

F7.9 Tables of electronegativities (Allred-Rochow scale) and ionic radii are given on pp. 82–85. Predict the most appropriate bond types for the AB compounds given below from amongst the following:
(i) almost entirely ionic;
(ii) ionic but with appreciable covalent character;
(iii) covalent but with appreciable ionic character;
(iv) almost entirely covalent.
Is RbF *(i)/(ii)/(iii)/(iv)*?

- -

A7.9 (i). With such a large electronegativity difference ($\Delta x = 3.2$), the bond is expected to be essentially ionic. The large singly-charged cation has only weak polarising power and fluoride ion is not very polarisable. Looked at in another way, the low ionisation potential of Rb, the high electron affinity, and the large electrostatic interaction energy between Rb^+ and F^- once formed, ensure that the production of an ionic compound is energetically very favourable.

F7.10 Is RaO *(i)/(ii)/(iii)/(iv)*?

- -

A7.10 (i) or (ii). The electronegativity difference is still large (2.5) and the ions are not very different in size from those of the preceding example. So the compound is essentially ionic. But the increased ionic charge means that polarisation effects will be more marked.

F7.11 Is BeTe *(i)/(ii)/(iii)/(iv)*?

- -

A7.11 (iii). The electronegativity difference Δx is low (0.5) and hence electron transfer will be incomplete. Interaction between Be^{2+} and Te^{2-} would give rise to extensive polarisation.

F7.12 Is NiAs *(i)/(ii)/(iii)/(iv)*?

- -

A7.12 (iii). Δx is low (0.4). In a hypothetical $Ni^{n+}-As^{n-}$ ionic situation, the small transition metal cation would strongly polarise the large anion (the estimated radius of As^{2-} is about 2Å, and that of As^{3-} is about 2.4Å).

F7.13 Is SiC *(i)/(ii)/(iii)/(iv)*?

- -

A7.13 (iii) or (iv). An ionic formation is clearly unrealistic, as too much energy would be required to produce Si^{4+}. Even if formed, Si^{4+} would catastrophically polarise C^{4-}. The electronegativity difference (0.8) probably suggests too high a degree of ionic character.

F7.14 Is IBr *(i)/(ii)/(iii)/(iv)*?

- -

A7.14 (iv). When two elements of rather high electronegativity combine together, there is little tendency for cation formation.

F7.15 Is AuCl *(i)/(ii)/(iii)/(iv)*?

- -

A7.15 (ii). Δx is quite large (1.4) and although Au^+ will be more polarising than K^+ of the same size, the amount of covalent character will not be very great.

F7.16 Is LaN *(i)/(ii)/(iii)/(iv)*?

- -

A7.16 (ii) or (iii). This is an example of a compound in which Δx is large (2.0) but polarisation effects are severe.

F7.17 From the examples above, the bond in a compound AB will be predominantly ionic if the electronegativity difference Δx is greater than *about 0.5/about 1.0/about 3.0.*

- -

A7.17 About 1.0.

F7.18 Exceptions can arise in cases where, although Δx is large, the polarisation effects in the ions that would be formed are *negligible/moderate/large*.

    A7.18 Large. See **F7.16**; $A^{3+}B^{3-}$ and $A^{4+}B^{4-}$ situations generally.

F7.19 Another case is when both A and B in AB are of rather low electronegativity. Thus electrons tend to be *strongly held by both atoms/easily released by both atoms*.

    A7.19 Easily released by both atoms.

F7.20 And the electrons *can move fairly freely in the solid/cluster between A and B/ cluster around either A or B*.

    A7.20 Can move fairly freely in the solid.

F7.21 This can be related to the high electrical and thermal conductivity of such solids. The resulting type of bond is termed *coordinate/metallic/van der Waals'*.

    A7.21 Metallic.

F7.22 Out of the following compounds, only the first four are found to possess metallic character: AlCo, AlLi, AuSn, BiTl, AlSb, BeTe, CuH, FeB, LaAs, RaTe, SnTe. From this information and the given table of electronegativities, it is possible to make the generalisation that metallic compounds are formed in AB systems if *the electronegativity difference Δx between A and B is $\leqslant 0.5$/the electronegativities of both A and B are $\leqslant 1.7$/the electronegativity of either A or B is $\leqslant 1.5$/the electronegativities of both A and B are $\leqslant 1.5$*.

    A7.22 The electronegativities of both A and B are $\leqslant 1.7$.

F7.23 Not all pairs of metals form compounds of definite composition. Sometimes the metals may be essentially immiscible; often solid solutions are formed. Also compounds may exist over a certain range of compositions, as in the case of β-brass, which persists as a homogeneous phase over the range $CuZn_{0.55}$ to $CuZn_{1.16}$. Generally however compounds are formed between metals from different parts of the periodic table. For example, a transition metal and a main group metal will probably form a compound. Predict which of the following systems are likely to produce compounds.

(a) Al–Cu   (b) Na–Pb   (c) Ag–Au   (d) K–Rb   (e) Ni–Sn
(f) Ca–Ni   (g) Mo–W   (h) Li–Hg

    A7.23 (a), (b), (e), (f) and (h) all form compounds. Note that sometimes when compound formation might be predicted on the basis of chemical dissimilarity, the metals are essentially immiscible, e.g. Fe–Hg.

F7.24 Notice that most AB compounds do not exist in the solid state as isolated molecules but as ionic arrays or as three-dimensional covalent network structures. Find out which of the examples in **F7.9–16** and **F7.22** contain discrete AB molecules in the solid.

    A7.24 Only one, IBr. (The structure of AuCl is not certain, but is probably three-dimensional.)

F7.25 If the coordination number of A in AB compounds is n, that of B will be *variable*/2n/0.5n/n.

    A7.25 n.

F7.26 The effect of charge separation or polarisation in each bond of such n-coordinate structures will be n *times/(1/n) times/the same as* that in the bond of the corresponding diatomic molecule **AB**.

    A7.26 $(1/n)$ times.

F7.27 Thus the total effect on each atom (or ion) of an n-coordinate structure will be *exactly the same as/larger than/smaller than* the effect predicted for the corresponding diatomic molecule **AB**.

    A7.27 Exactly the same (since each atom has n bonds, contributing $1/n$ times the effect). The arguments developed concerning bond type are therefore valid whatever the structure of solid AB, provided that the coordination is regular.

F7.28 Let us now consider compounds of the general type AB_2. In the same way as before, classify all the following compounds into one of the following types, making use of electronegativity coefficients, polarising powers and any other relevant information:

    (i) almost entirely ionic;
    (ii) ionic but with appreciable covalent character;
    (iii) covalent but with appreciable ionic character;
    (iv) almost entirely covalent;
    (v) metallic.

Is BaF_2 *(i)/(ii)/(iii)/(iv)/(v)*?

A7.28 (i). With an electronegativity difference Δx of 3.1, charge transfer is very marked. Also polarisation effects are not expected to be large.

F7.29 Is CdI_2 *(i)/(ii)/(iii)/(iv)/(v)?*

A7.29 (ii) or (iii). Δx is small (0.7), also polarisation is considerable.

F7.30 Is $AuAl_2$ *(i)/(ii)/(iii)/(iv)/(v)?*

A7.30 (v). The electronegativities of both Au and Al are low; compare F7.23.

F7.31 Is NO_2 *(i)/(ii)/(iii)/(iv)/(v)?*

A7.31 (iv). The electronegativities of both N and O are high, and Δx is small (0.4).

F7.32 Is TiO_2 *(i)/(ii)/(iii)/(iv)/(v)?*

A7.32 (i) or (ii). The electronegativity difference is large (2.2) but the relatively small Ti^{4+} ion will polarise the anions appreciably.

F7.33 Is SiO_2 *(i)/(ii)/(iii)/(iv)/(v)?*

A7.33 (ii) or (iii). An intermediate case, in which $\Delta x = 1.8$. If Si^{4+} were present, it would be very strongly polarising.

F7.34 Is $PdCl_2$ *(i)/(ii)/(iii)/(iv)/(v)?*

A7.34 (ii) or (iii). Another intermediate example with $\Delta x = 1.4$ in which the transition metal ion Pd^{2+} is markedly polarising, despite its rather large size.

F7.35 Is Be_2C *(i)/(ii)/(iii)/(iv)/(v)?*

A7.35 (iii). Here $\Delta x = 1.0$. Note that hypothetical $Be_2^{2+}C^{4-}$ would be severely polarised.

F7.36 Which of the compounds in F7.28–35 has a molecular structure in the solid state?

A7.36 NO_2. Other AB_2 examples are SO_2, CO_2, SCl_2, OF_2.

F7.37 Which of the compounds in **F7.28–35** has a layer structure in the solid state?

> **A7.37** CdI_2. Other AB_2 examples are $NiCl_2$ (and many other transition metal halides), MoS_2, HgI_2.

F7.38 Which of the compounds in **F7.28–35** has a chain structure in the solid state?

> **A7.38** $PdCl_2$. Other AB_2 examples (with different chain structures) are SiS_2, $BeCl_2$, $CuCl_2$.

F7.39 We now consider representative AB_3 compounds. If A is *n*-coordinate, B will have a coordination number of n/(n/3)/3n.

> **A7.39** $n/3$. It is therefore unusual for B in AB_3 to be even 3-coordinate.

F7.40 As before, classify the following compounds into the categories given in **F7.28**. Is BF_3 *(i)/(ii)/(iii)/(iv)/(v)*?

> **A7.40** (iii). The electronegativity difference Δx is large (2.1), but as three fluorines are attached to each boron, the resulting bond polarity in each bond is not as large as it would be in a compound AB of similar Δx value. Note that B^{3+} is expected to be very strongly polarising.

F7.41 Is $CrCl_3$ *(i)/(ii)/(iii)/(iv)/(v)*?

> **A7.41** (iii). The electronegativity difference is moderate (1.2). Hypothetical $Cr^{3+}Cl_3^-$ would be extensively polarised.

F7.42 Is ReO_3 *(i)/(ii)/(iii)/(iv)/(v)*?

> **A7.42** (ii). Here $\Delta x = 2.0$. Large Re^{VI} is quite strongly polarising.

F7.43 Is $LaCl_3$ *(i)/(ii)/(iii)/(iv)/(v)*?

> **A7.43** (i) or (ii). Note that although Δx (1.7) is actually less than in BF_3 the large La^{3+} ion is far less strongly polarising.

F7.44 Is PI_3 *(i)/(ii)/(iii)/(iv)/(v)*?

> **A7.44** (iv). Here Δx is only 0.1, and both P and I are quite electronegative.

F7.45 Is Al_3Zr *(i)/(ii)/(iii)/(iv)/(v)*?

- -

    A7.45 (v). Both Al and Zr have low electronegativities.

F7.46 Only two of the compounds in **F7.40–45** show appreciable ionic character (ReO_3, $LaCl_3$), while one ($CrCl_3$) has a layer structure in the solid state, and two (BF_3, PI_3) are molecular.

Compare this distribution with the situation in AB and AB_2 compounds. It appears that as n in AB_n increases, the tendency to form molecular compounds *increases/ remains the same/decreases*.

- -

    A7.46 Increases. Only the largest cations M^{n+} fail to produce extensive polarisation when n is large.

F7.47 Many AB_4 and almost all AB_5 compounds are molecular: the exceptions are most likely to be *oxides/fluorides/sulphides*.

- -

    A7.47 Fluorides. Here the bond polarities are greatest and the polarisability is lowest. Also MO_4 implies M(VIII), found only in molecular OsO_4 and RuO_4. Simple compounds of the type MO_5, MS_5, MO_6, etc. are not known (but see **F7.52**).

F7.48 Almost all AB_6 compounds of known structure are molecular, apart from the possibility of metallic alloys when the electronegativity of both A and B is *low/high*, and the special cases mentioned in **F7.52**.

- -

    A7.48 Low.

F7.49 Notice that in a compound such as UF_6, the electronegativity difference Δx suggests that each U–F bond will have *almost no charge separation/appreciable charge separation*.

- -

    A7.49 Appreciable charge separation. $\Delta x = 2.9$, but six bonds are also involved. The 6th ionisation energy of uranium is sufficiently large to ensure that $U^{6+}F_6^-$ could not be formed.

F7.50 The partial negative charges on fluorine in such molecules as PF_5, SF_6 and UF_6 imply that the molecules will tend to *attract/repel* each other.

- -

    A7.50 Repel.

F7.51 The intermolecular forces and boiling points will therefore be unusually *low/ high*.

      A7.51 Low.

F7.52 Some solid compounds AB_n in which n is large contain clusters or closely-bound groups of B atoms. Some examples are: PbN_6, with Pb^{2+} and N_3^- ions; KC_8, with K atoms between graphite layers; UB_{12}, with clusters of twelve boron atoms; BaO_4, with Ba^{2+} and O_2^- ions; alloys such as KZn_{13}, with K embedded in a matrix of Zn atoms. Apart from the metallic alloys of this class (in which both A and B are of a low electronegativity), the clustered atoms in such compounds are *small atoms of low electronegativity/large atoms of high electronegativity/small atoms of high electronegativity*.

      A7.52 Small atoms of high electronegativity.

Now repeat the programme test on p. 71, and mark it as before. If you score greater than 16 you have successfully completed this programme.

Summary

1.   Large electronegativity differences between elements are associated with essentially ionic bonding between these atoms.

2.   Extensive polarisation of ions leads to covalent bond character and is particularly evident when small highly charged cations are bonded to large highly charged anions.

3.   The bond in a compound AB will be predominantly ionic if Δx is greater than about 1.0. Exceptions can arise in cases where, although Δx is large, the polarisation effects in the ions that would be formed are large.

4.   Another important case is when both A and B are of rather low electronegativity; the electrons tend to be easily released by both atoms and can move fairly freely in the solid, a situation which is associated with metallic bonding. Metallic compounds are formed if the electronegativities of both A and B are < 1.7.

5.   Not all pairs of metals form compounds of definite composition. Sometimes the metals may be essentially immiscible, or solid solutions are formed, or compounds may exist over a limited range of compositions. Generally compounds are formed between metals from different parts of the periodic table although there are some cases of dissimilar metals being immiscible.

6.   Most AB compounds do not exist in the solid state as isolated molecules but as ionic arrays or as three-dimensional covalent network structures. However, the arguments developed concerning bond type are valid whatever the structure of solid AB.

7. As n in AB_n increases, the tendency to form molecular compounds increases. Only the largest cations M^{n+} fail to produce extensive polarisation when n is large, unless the anion is small (F^-, O^{2-}).

8. Intermolecular forces and boiling points will be unusually low in compounds AB_n in which the anions are formed from electronegative elements. This is due to the electrostatic repulsions between the resulting partial negative charges at the peripheries of the molecules.

9. Some solid compounds AB_n in which n is large contain clusters of closely-bound groups of B atoms. Apart from metallic alloys of this class (in which both A and B are of low electronegativity), the clustered atoms in such compounds are small atoms of high electronegativity.

Chapter 8

Tables for Use with Inorganic Chemistry Learning Programmes

Professor B.J.Aylett

Westfield College, University of London, London NW3 7ST

Notes

1. Values given in these tables are rounded off to give sufficient precision for most purposes.

2. SI units are used for energy (1 kJ mol^{-1} ≡ 0.24 kcal mol^{-1} ≡ 0.0104 eV); atomic distances are given in Å (1Å ≡ 100pm).

3. Values have been selected from a number of standard reference texts; a number of discrepancies exist, but in no case do these affect the general principles laid down in the programmes.

4. Atomic radii refer to covalent single-bond radii, mainly those derived by Pauling.

5. Ionic radii are generally those of Pauling rather than those of Goldschmidt. At this level of precision, only with H$^-$, Li$^+$ and possibly Mg^{2+} is the difference significant.

Size and Electronegativity

Element	Atomic number	Electronegativity coeffs. Pauling	Allred-Rochow	Atom radius (Å) see note 4	Ion	Ion radius (Å) see note 5
Ac	89	–	1.0	1.7 (est.)	Ac^{3+}	1.2
Ag	47	1.9	1.4	1.3	Ag$^+$	1.2
Al	13	1.6	1.5	1.2	Al^{3+}	0.5
Ar	18	–	–	1.0	–	–
As	33	2.2	2.2	1.2	As^{3+}	0.6
					As^{3-}	2.4 (est.)
Au	79	2.5	1.4	1.3	Au$^+$	1.4
					Au^{3+}	0.9
B	5	2.0	2.0	0.8	B^{3+}	0.25
Ba	56	0.9	1.0	2.0	Ba^{2+}	1.4
Be	4	1.6	1.5	0.9	Be^{2+}	0.35
Bi	83	2.0	1.7	1.5	Bi^{3+}	1.0
					Bi^{5+}	0.7

Size and Electronegativity—*continued*

Element	Atomic number	Electronegativity coeffs. Pauling	Allred-Rochow	Atom radius (Å)	Ion	Ion radius (Å)
Br	35	3.0	2.7	1.1	Br^-	2.0
C	6	2.6	2.5	0.8	C^{4+}	0.15 (est.)
					C^{4-}	1.9 (est.)
Ca	20	1.0	1.0	1.7	Ca^{2+}	1.0
Cd	48	1.7	1.5	1.5	Cd^{2+}	1.0
Ce	58	—	1.1	1.7	Ce^{3+}	1.1
					Ce^{4+}	1.0
Cl	17	3.2	2.8	1.0	Cl^-	1.8
Co	27	1.9	1.7	1.2	Co^{2+}	0.7
					Co^{3+}	0.6
Cr	24	1.7	1.6	1.2	Cr^{2+}	0.8
					Cr^{3+}	0.6
Cs	55	0.8	0.9	2.4	Cs^+	1.7
Cu	29	1.9	1.8	1.2	Cu^+	1.0
					Cu^{2+}	0.7
Dy	66	—	1.1	1.6	Dy^{3+}	0.9
Er	68	—	1.1	1.6	Er^{3+}	0.9
Eu	63	—	1.0	1.9	Eu^{3+}	1.0
F	9	4.0	4.1	0.6	F^-	1.3
Fe	26	1.8	1.6	1.2	Fe^{2+}	0.7
					Fe^{3+}	0.6
Fr	87	—	0.9	—	Fr^+	1.8 (est.)
Ga	31	1.8	1.8	1.3	Ga^{3+}	0.6
Gd	64	—	1.1	1.6	Gd^{3+}	1.0
Ge	32	2.0	2.0	1.2	Ge^{4+}	0.5 (est.)
H	1	2.1	2.2	0.3	H^+	*ca.* 0
					H^-	1.3–1.5
He	2	—	—	0.3	—	—
Hf	72	—	1.2	1.4	Hf^{4+}	0.8
Hg	80	2.0	1.4	1.5	Hg^{2+}	1.1
Ho	67	—	1.1	1.6	Ho^{3+}	0.9
I	53	2.7	2.2	1.3	I^-	2.2
In	49	1.8	1.5	1.4	In^{3+}	0.8
Ir	77	2.2	1.6	1.3	Ir^{4+}	0.7
K	19	0.8	0.9	2.0	K^+	1.3
Kr	36	—	—	1.1	—	—
La	57	—	1.1	1.7	La^{3+}	1.1
Li	3	1.0	1.0	1.2	Li^+	0.7
Lu	71	—	1.1	1.6	Lu^{3+}	0.9
Mg	12	1.3	1.2	1.4	Mg^{2+}	0.7
Mn	25	1.6	1.6	1.2	Mn^{2+}	0.8

Size and Electronegativity—*continued*

Element	Atomic number	Electronegativity coeffs. Pauling	Allred-Rochow	Atom radius (Å)	Ion	Ion radius (Å)
Mo	42	2.2	1.3	1.3	Mo^{0+}	0.6 (est.)
N	7	3.0	3.1	0.7	N^{3+}	0.15 (est.)
					N^{3-}	1.7 (est.)
Na	11	0.9	1.0	1.5	Na^+	1.0
Nb	41	—	1.2	1.3	Nb^{5+}	0.7 (est.)
Nd	60	—	1.1	1.6	Nd^{3+}	1.0
Ne	10	—	—	0.7	—	—
Ni	28	1.9	1.8	1.2	Ni^{2+}	0.7
Np	93	—	1.2	—	Np^{3+}	1.1
O	8	3.4	3.5	0.7	O^{2-}	1.4
Os	76	—	1.5	1.3	Os^{4+}	0.7
P	15	2.2	2.1	1.1	P^{3+}	0.4 (est.)
					P^{3-}	2.1 (est.)
Pa	91	—	1.1	—	Pa^{4+}	1.0
Pb	82	2.3	1.6	1.5	Pb^{2+}	1.2
Pd	46	2.2	1.4	1.3	Pd^{2+}	0.8
Pm	61	—	1.1	1.6	Pm^{3+}	1.1
Po	84	—	1.8	1.5	Po^{2-}	2.4 (est.)
Pr	59	—	1.1	1.6	Pr^{3+}	1.1
Pt	78	2.3	1.4	1.3	Pt^{2+}	0.8
Pu	94	—	1.2	—	Pu^{3+}	1.1
Ra	88	—	1.0	2.0 (est.)	Ra^{2+}	1.4
Rb	37	0.8	0.9	2.2	Rb^+	1.5
Re	75	—	1.5	1.3	Re^{6+}	0.6 (est.)
					Re^{7+}	0.6 (est.)
Rh	45	2.3	1.5	1.3	Rh^{3+}	0.7
Ru	44	—	1.4	1.3	Ru^{4+}	0.7
S	16	2.6	2.4	1.0	S^{2-}	1.8
Sb	51	2.0	1.8	1.4	Sb^{3+}	0.8
					Sb^{3-}	2.5 (est.)
Sc	21	1.4	1.2	1.4	Sc^{3+}	0.8
Se	34	2.6	2.5	1.2	Se^{2-}	2.0
Si	14	1.9	1.7	1.2	Si^{4+}	0.4 (est.)
Sm	62	—	1.1	1.6	Sm^{3+}	1.0
Sn	50	2.0	1.7	1.4	Sn^{2+}	0.9
					Sn^{4+}	0.7
Sr	38	1.0	1.0	1.9	Sr^{2+}	1.1
Ta	73	—	1.3	1.3	Ta^{5+}	0.7 (est.)
Tb	65	—	1.1	1.6	Tb^{3+}	0.9
Tc	43	—	1.4	1.3	Tc^{7+}	0.6 (est.)
Te	52	—	2.0	1.4	Te^{2-}	2.2

Size and Electronegativity—*continued*

Element	Atomic number	Pauling	Allred-Rochow	Atom radius (Å)	Ion	Ion radius (Å)
Th	90	–	1.1	1.7	Th^{4+}	1.0
Ti	22	1.5	1.3	1.3	Ti^{4+}	0.9
Tl	81	2.0	1.4	1.5	Tl^{3+}	1.0 (est.)
Tm	69	–	1.1	1.6	Tm^{3+}	0.9
U	92	–	1.2	1.4	U^{6+}	0.8 (est.)
V	23	1.6	1.5	1.2	V^{2+}	0.9
W	74	2.4	1.4	1.3	W^{6+}	0.6 (est.)
Xe	54	–	–	1.3	–	–
Y	39	1.2	1.1	1.6	Y^{3+}	0.9
Yb	70	–	1.1	1.6	Yb^{3+}	0.9
Zn	30	1.7	1.7	1.3	Zn^{2+}	0.7
Zr	40	1.3	1.2	1.5	Zr^{4+}	0.8

Ionisation Energies

Element	Atomic number	I	II	III	IV	V	VI
H	1	1310	–	–	–	–	–
He	2	2380	5270	–	–	–	–
Li	3	520	7290	11800	–	–	–
Be	4	900	1760	14800	21000	–	–
B	5	815	2420	3660	25000	32800	–
C	6	1090	2360	4600	6230	37800	47000
N	7	1410	2850	4590	7470	9430	48800
O	8	1320	3400	5320	7450	11000	13250
F	9	1680	3380	6050	8410	11000	15100
Ne	10	2100	3960	–	–	–	–
Na	11	500	4560	–	–	–	–
Mg	12	755	1460	7710	–	–	–
Al	13	585	1820	2750	11600	–	–
Si	14	795	1580	3240	4350	16200	–
P	15	1070	1900	2910	4960	6270	–
S	16	1000	2260	3390	4560	6980	8450
Cl	17	1250	2300	3850	5250	6540	9340
Ar	18	1525	2670	3950	5770	–	–
K	19	420	3080	4600	5880	–	–
Ca	20	595	1150	4940	6480	–	–
Sc	21	640	1250	2390	7140	–	–

Ionisation energies (kJ mol⁻¹)

Ionisation Energies–*continued*

Element	Atomic number	I	II	III	IV	V	VI
				Ionisation energies (kJ mol^{-1})			
Ti	22	670	1320	2720	4170	9620	–
V	23	655	1380	2880	4600	6170	12800
Cr	24	660	1600	2990	4760	7050	8690
Mn	25	725	1510	3260	5160	7330	9720
Fe	26	765	1570	2960	–	–	–
Co	27	760	2070	3240	–	–	–
Ni	28	745	1760	3400	–	–	–
Cu	29	755	1960	3560	–	–	–
Zn	30	910	1740	3840	–	–	–
Ga	31	580	1980	2970	6200	–	–
Ge	32	770	1540	3310	4410	9020	–
As	33	955	1960	2740	4860	6040	12250
Se	34	945	2080	3100	4140	6550	7860
Br	35	1150	2090	3460	4820	5800	8400
Kr	36	1360	2380	3570	–	–	–
Rb	37	410	2660	3860	–	–	–
Sr	38	555	1070	–	5440	–	–
Y	39	620	1190	1990	–	–	–
Zr	40	670	1270	2230	3320	–	–
Nb	41	670	1390	2420	3700	4830	–
Mo	42	690	1560	2620	4480	–	–
Tc	43	705	1480	–	–	–	–
Ru	44	715	1620	2750	–	–	–
Rh	45	730	1750	3000	–	–	–
Pd	46	810	1880	3180	4710	–	–
Ag	47	735	2080	3360	–	–	–
Cd	48	875	1630	3620	–	–	–
In	49	565	1820	2710	5240	–	–
Sn	50	715	1420	2950	3940	7820	–
Sb	51	840	1590	2420	4270	5380	10300
Te	52	875	1800	3020	3690	5800	6950
I	53	1020	1850	3030	4020	5020	7420
Xe	54	1170	2050	3100	–	–	–
Cs	55	380	2420	–	–	–	–
Ba	56	510	965	–	–	–	–
La	57	545	1110	1860	–	–	–
Hf	72	675	1440	–	–	–	–
Ta	73	765	1570	–	–	–	–
W	74	775	1710	–	–	–	–
Re	75	765	1600	–	–	–	–
Os	76	840	1630	–	–	–	–

Ionisation Energies–*continued*

Element	Atomic number	Ionisation energies (kJ mol^{-1})					
		I	II	III	IV	V	VI
Ir	77	840	—	—	—	—	—
Pt	78	880	1860	—	—	—	—
Au	79	895	1980	—	—	—	—
Hg	80	1010	1820	3300	—	—	—
Tl	81	595	1970	2880	4900	—	—
Pb	82	720	1460	3080	4080	6720	—
Bi	83	710	1610	2470	4380	5400	9070
Rn	86	1040	—	—	—	—	—
Ra	88	515	985	—	—	—	—

Electronic Configurations and Electron Affinity

Element	Atomic Number	Configuration	Electron Affinity (kJ mol^{-1})	Element	Atomic Number	Configuration	Electron Affinity (kJ mol^{-1})
H	1	$1s^1$	73	I	53	[Kr] $5s^2 4d^{10} 5p^5$	298
He	2	$1s^2$		Xe	54	[Kr] $5s^2 4d^{10} 5p^6$	
Li	3	[He] $2s^1$	50	Cs	55	[Xe] $6s^1$	
Be	4	[He] $2s^2$	-59	Ba	56	[Xe] $6s^2$	
B	5	[He] $2s^2 2p^1$	34	La	57	[Xe] $6s^2 5d^1$	
C	6	[He] $2s^2 2p^2$	109	Ce	58	[Xe] $6s^2 5d^0 4f^2$	
N	7	[He] $2s^2 2p^3$	-25	Pr	59	[Xe] $6s^2 5d^0 4f^3$	
O	8	[He] $2s^2 2p^4$	142	Nd	60	[Xe] $6s^2 5d^0 4f^4$	
F	9	[He] $2s^2 2p^5$	334	Pm	61	[Xe] $6s^2 5d^0 4f^5$	
Ne	10	[He] $2s^2 2p^6$		Sm	62	[Xe] $6s^2 5d^0 4f^6$	
Na	11	[Ne] $3s^1$	73	Eu	63	[Xe] $6s^2 5d^0 4f^7$	
Mg	12	[Ne] $3s^2$	-29	Gd	64	[Xe] $6s^2 5d^1 4f^7$	
Al	13	[Ne] $3s^2 3p^1$	50	Tb	65	[Xe] $6s^2 5d^0 4f^9$	
Si	14	[Ne] $3s^2 3p^2$	134	Dy	66	[Xe] $6s^2 5d^0 4f^{10}$	
P	15	[Ne] $3s^2 3p^3$	76	Ho	67	[Xe] $6s^2 5d^0 4f^{11}$	
S	16	[Ne] $3s^2 3p^4$	202	Er	68	[Xe] $6s^2 5d^0 4f^{12}$	
Cl	17	[Ne] $3s^2 3p^5$	356	Tm	69	[Xe] $6s^2 5d^0 4f^{13}$	
Ar	18	[Ne] $3s^2 3p^6$		Yb	70	[Xe] $6s^2 5d^0 4f^{14}$	
K	19	[Ar] $4s^1$	67	Lu	71	[Xe] $6s^2 5d^1 4f^{14}$	
Ca	20	[Ar] $4s^2$		Hf	72	[Xe] $6s^2 5d^2 4f^{14}$	
Sc	21	[Ar] $4s^2 3d^1$		Ta	73	[Xe] $6s^2 5d^3 4f^{14}$	
Ti	22	[Ar] $4s^2 3d^2$		W	74	[Xe] $6s^2 5d^4 4f^{14}$	
V	23	[Ar] $4s^2 3d^3$		Re	75	[Xe] $6s^2 5d^5 4f^{14}$	
Cr	24	[Ar] $4s^1 3d^5$		Os	76	[Xe] $6s^2 5d^6 4f^{14}$	

Z	Element	Configuration	Value
27	Co	[Ar] $4s^2 3d^7$	
28	Ni	[Ar] $4s^2 3d^8$	
29	Cu	[Ar] $4s^1 3d^{10}$	
30	Zn	[Ar] $4s^2 3d^{10}$	
31	Ga	[Ar] $4s^2 3d^{10} 4p^1$	147
32	Ge	[Ar] $4s^2 3d^{10} 4p^2$	
33	As	[Ar] $4s^2 3d^{10} 4p^3$	
34	Se	[Ar] $4s^2 3d^{10} 4p^4$	214
35	Br	[Ar] $4s^2 3d^{10} 4p^5$	328
36	Kr	[Ar] $4s^2 3d^{10} 4p^6$	
37	Rb	[Kr] $5s^1$	
38	Sr	[Kr] $5s^2$	
39	Y	[Kr] $5s^2 4d^1$	
40	Zr	[Kr] $5s^2 4d^2$	
41	Nb	[Kr] $5s^1 4d^4$	
42	Mo	[Kr] $5s^1 4d^5$	
43	Tc	[Kr] $5s^2 4d^5$	
44	Ru	[Kr] $5s^1 4d^7$	
45	Rh	[Kr] $5s^1 4d^8$	
46	Pd	[Kr] $5s^0 4d^{10}$	
47	Ag	[Kr] $5s^1 4d^{10}$	193
48	Cd	[Kr] $5s^2 4d^{10}$	
49	In	[Kr] $5s^2 4d^{10} 5p^1$	
50	Sn	[Kr] $5s^2 4d^{10} 5p^2$	
51	Sb	[Kr] $5s^2 4d^{10} 5p^3$	
52	Te	[Kr] $5s^2 4d^{10} 5p^4$	223

Z	Element	Configuration	Value
79	Au	[Xe] $6s^1 5d^{10} 4f^{14}$	274
80	Hg	[Xe] $6s^2 5d^{10} 4f^{14}$	147
81	Tl	[Xe] $6s^2 5d^{10} 4f^{14} 6p^1$	
82	Pb	[Xe] $6s^2 5d^{10} 4f^{14} 6p^2$	
83	Bi	[Xe] $6s^2 5d^{10} 4f^{14} 6p^3$	252
84	Po	[Xe] $6s^2 5d^{10} 4f^{14} 6p^4$	
85	At	[Xe] $6s^2 5d^{10} 4f^{14} 6p^5$	
86	Rn	[Xe] $6s^2 5d^{10} 4f^{14} 6p^6$	
87	Fr	[Rn] $7s^1$	
88	Ra	[Rn] $7s^2$	
89	Ac	[Rn] $7s^2 6d^1$	
90	Th	[Rn] $7s^2 6d^2$	
91	Pa	[Rn] $7s^2 6d^1 5f^2$	
92	U	[Rn] $7s^2 6d^1 5f^3$	
93	Np	[Rn] $7s^2 6d^0 5f^5$	
94	Pu	[Rn] $7s^2 6d^0 5f^6$	
95	Am	[Rn] $7s^2 6d^0 5f^7$	
96	Cm	[Rn] $7s^2 6d^1 5f^7$	
97	Bk	[Rn] $7s^2 6d^1 5f^8$	
98	Cf	[Rn] $7s^2 6d^0 5f^{10}$	
99	Es	[Rn] $7s^2 6d^0 5f^{11}$	
100	Fm	[Rn] $7s^2 6d^0 5f^{12}$	
101	Md	[Rn] $7s^2 6d^0 5f^{13}$	
102	—	[Rn] $7s^2 6d^0 5f^{14}$	
103	Lw	[Rn] $7s^2 6d^1 5f^{14}$	

Answers and Scores
to the Programme Tests

Chapter 1: Electronic Configuration of Atoms: The Periodic Table

1. If $n = 3$, l may be 0, 1 or 2.   (1), (1), (1)
    For $l = 0$, $m = 0$;   (1)
         $l = 1$, $m = +1$, 0 or -1;   (2)
         $l = 2$, $m = +2$, $+1$, 0, -1 or -2.   (2)

2. The Pauli Exclusion principle states that in an atom no two
    electrons can have the same set of values for all four quantum
    numbers.   (2)

3. An orbital may contain 0, 1 or 2 electrons.   (2)
    If an orbital contains 2 electrons, spins must be paired.   (1)

4. The symbol 3d indicates that for this particular orbital $n = 3$
    and $l = 2$.   (1)

5. $1s^2 2s^2 2p^1$.   (1)

6. Electrons occupy the orbitals $n = x$ while the orbitals $n = (x - 1)$
    are incompletely filled.   (1)

7. Electrons occupy the orbitals $n = x$ while the orbitals $n = (x - 2)$
    are incompletely filled.   (1)

8. All have a valency shell configuration $s^2 p^6$.   (1)

9. All have a single electron in an s orbital in the valency shell.   (1)

The maximum possible score for this test is 19.

Chapter 2: Atomic Size and Coordination Number

1. $3s^2 3p^1$.   (1)

2. Since the radial probability distribution extends to infinity, there is
    no volume which contains all the electrons and therefore no definite atom
    atomic radius. The most significant parameter in the radial distribution
    is the radius at which there is a maximum probability of finding the
    valence electrons, but this is not the same as values measured
    empirically from bond length data.   (2)

3. H, 0.3Å; C, 0.8Å; I, 1.3Å.   (3)

4. X-ray diffraction, neutron diffraction, microwave spectra, dipole
   moments, infrared spectra, etc. (2)
5. (i) Extent of ionic or covalent character.
   (ii) Coordination number.
   (iii) Multiple covalent bonding. (3)
6. Ionisation energy decreases and the numerical value of the electron
   affinity decreases as atomic size increases. (2)
7. (a) Cl^- (b) Ca (c) Fe^{2+} (d) As (e) Al
   (f) Ti^{2+} (g) Zr (h) Cl^- (i) Cs^+ (j) Na^+ (10)
8. The coordination number is the number of nearest neighbour ions
   surrounding the one in question. (The same concept can be applied to
   covalently bonded atoms.) (1)
9. 3 trigonal; 4 tetrahedral; 6 octahedral; 8 cubic. (4)
10. Anions around a cation, since the cation will usually be the smaller. (1)
11. The critical feature is the octahedral coordination of Ti^{4+} (by O^{2-}) and
    the lower limit of the radius ratio is 0.414. (1)
12. Bond angles in a trigonal bipyramid are $90°$ and $120°$. Therefore ions
    will touch first in the $90°$ position. $90°$ bond angles are characteristic
    of the octahedron and the square, both of which have the limiting radius
    radius of 0.414. This value will therefore apply to the trigonal
    bipyramid. (2)
13. The van der Waals radius is half the minimum distance between two
    non-bonded atoms of the same kind. (1)

The maximum possible score for this test is 33.

Chapter 3: Electronic Screening and Effective Nuclear Charge

1. The outer electrons feel the effect of the total charge inside them, this
   being the sum of the actual nuclear charge (positive) and the charges
   (negative) of the inner electrons. In effect, the inner electrons repel the
   outer electrons, thus screening them from the nucleus. (3)
2. $Z^* = Z - \sigma$. (1)
3. $Z^* = +1$ when $\sigma = Z - 1$ (perfect screening). (1)
4. Perfect screening unrealistically assumes that all the electron density of
   inner electrons is confined within a finite sphere and that the electron
   density of outer electrons is entirely outside that sphere. (2)
5. (a) 0 (b) $\approx 1/3$ (c) 1.0 (1), (1), (1)
6. Inner electrons are less shielded than outer electrons. (1)
7. d and f orbitals penetrate closer towards the nucleus as reflected in
   the way the radial electron densities vary. (1)
8. 4s electrons feel a smaller value of Z^* than do 3d electrons and
   therefore ionise first. This is because the 3d electrons count as inner
   electrons when calculating Z^* for 4s, but as electrons in the same
   group when calculating Z^* for 3d. (3)
9. (a) Increase. (1)
10. (c) Remain about the same. (1)

11. (a) Sulphur;   (b) nickel;   (c) about the same. $(1), (1), (1)$

12. Effective nuclear charge determines the force which binds the outermost electrons to the atom, and therefore determines the energy (ionisation energy) required to remove the outermost electron and also its average distance (atomic radius) from the nucleus. (3)

13.

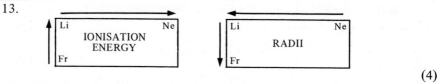

(4)

14. After vanadium and nickel there are discontinuities. (2)

15. The Allred-Rochow electronegativity scale is defined by
$$x = Z^* e^2 / r^2 \qquad [Z^* e^2 / 4\pi\epsilon_0 r^2 \text{ in SI units}]$$ (2)

16. Ionic radius is inversely proportional to Z^*, and therefore Pauling divided measured interionic distances in the inverse ratio of the Z^* values. This only works for isoelectronic ions, since the proportionality parameter is constant only for such types of ion. (2)

17. $E \propto -(Z^*/n^*)^2$ (2)

The maximum possible score for this test is 35.

Chapter 4: Ionisation Energies and Electron Affinities

1. Ionisation energy (E_i) is the energy which must be put into a system to produce the desired cation. Thus the first E_i of an atom is the energy required to remove an electron from an atom to form the positive ion. (1)

2. In general the more easily an element loses its electrons the more reactive it is. Also a large discontinuity in the magnitude of consecutive E_i's corresponds to the maximum valency of the species. (2)

3. If it is difficult to remove electrons, then usually anions or covalent species result from the addition of electrons. (1)

4. Calcium forms Ca^{2+}. The energy needed to form Ca^{3+} is prohibitively high and Ca^+ is unstable (towards disproportionation). (1)

5. Valency corresponds to the combining power of a unit and is closely related to its electron configuration. Using valency it is usually possible to say in what numeric ratio atoms will react. (1)

6. TlH_3 is unknown. Tl^{III} is strongly oxidising and H^- is strongly reducing. It is unlikely therefore that these will be mutually compatible. (2)

7. Energy must be added to form H^- and the species is reactive giving out this energy on reaction. When F^- is formed, energy is released and F^- is therefore stable. (2)

8. Si^{4+} is small with a large charge and so is an extremely reactive species and will react (hydrate) in aqueous solution. Thus it usually precipitates as hydrated silica, "$SiO_2 . 2H_2O$". (2)

7. (a) Sulphur; (b) copper; (c) phosphorus; (d) sulphur.

$$(1), (1), (1), (1)$$

8. (a) Dipole moment; (c) Partial ionic bond character;
   (d) bond energy; (e) nucleophilic character. $(1), (1), (1), (1)$

9. In NaO_2 the oxygen molecule has accepted an electron to form O_2^-, while in $O_2 PtF_6$ it has lost an electron to form PtF_6^- and O_2^+.
   E_i's and E_a's apply to molecules also. (2)

10. The values of E_i for carbon indicate a maximum valency of 4, and this agrees well with a valency of 3 for B and 5 for N. (3)

11. Extra electrons are added to orbitals further from the nucleus to give a bigger atom. (1)

12. The amount by which the additional electrons of these atoms are protected from the attractive pull of the nucleus decreases due to the shapes of their orbitals. This means that they experience a greater attraction to the nucleus and results in a decrease in atomic radius. (2)

13. From Li to Na electrons go into s and p orbitals, while between Rb and Cs, p and d orbitals are filled. d Orbitals obscure (shield) the nuclear charge less effectively than s or p orbitals. Hence the Cs 6s electron is affected by a relatively greater charge with respect to the Rb 5s electron than is the Na 3s electron relative to the Li 2s electron. This results in a smaller increase in size. (2)

14. Ion size and charge are the main factors. (2)

15. $E^0 = \dfrac{RT}{nF} \ln K$. (1)

The maximum possible score for this test is 25.

Chapter 5: Electronegativity

1. Within a covalent molecule some atoms have a greater tendency to attract the shared electrons than others. This electron attracting power of an atom in a molecule is known as its electronegativity. (3)

2. (b) Electron affinity and (c) ionisation energy. $(1), (1)$

3. (a) Mulliken: $x = \frac{1}{2}(E_i + E_a)$

   (b) Pauling: $(x_A - x_B) = \sqrt{(\Delta_{AB}/23.06)}$
      where $\Delta_{AB} = D_{AB} - \frac{1}{2}(D_{A_2} + D_{B_2})$
      (values expressed in kcal mol^{-1}). $(1), (2)$

4. Electronegativity is distinguished from electron affinity in that the former quantity refers to atoms in molecules, whereas the latter quantity refers to isolated gaseous atoms. (2)

5. Ionisation energy is more important than electron affinity in determining electronegativity. (1)

6. Electronegativity increases as shown. (4)

9. $H = 2, F = 4, Cs = 1, N = 3, Mn = 1.5.$ (1), (1), (1), (1), (1)

10. Non-metals are more electronegative than metals.   (1)

11. (b) B–N and H–F bonds should be formed since $N > H$
    and $F > B$ in electronegativity.   (2)

12. Nitrogen, oxygen and fluorine are the most likely elements
    to form strong hydrogen bonds.   (3)

13. (a) $MgCl_2$;   (b) PbO_2.   (1), (1)

The maximum possible score for this test is 36.

Chapter 6: Polarisation and Polarisability

1. (a) I^-;   (b) Fe^{2+}.   (1), (1)

2. Fe^{3+}.   (1)

3. Cl^-.   (1)

4. (a) K–F;   (b) Fe^{2+}–X.   (1), (1)

5. Cu^+. The poor shielding characteristics of the d orbitals allow the
    greater effective nuclear charge to enhance the polarising power of
    this ion.   (2)

6. LiCl.   (1)

7. CaI_2 (575°C) $<$ $CaBr_2$ (730°C) $<$ $CaCl_2$ (772°C) $<$ CaF_2 (1382°C)   (1)

8. (a) $F < Cl < Br < I$; (b) I (2.7) $<$ Br (3.0) $<$ Cl (3.2) $<$ F (4.0)
    (Pauling values).   (1)

9. The two ions in each of the pairs: Li^+ and Mg^{2+}, Be^{2+} and Al^{3+}, B^{3+}
    and Si^{4+} have similar polarising powers.   (1)

10. (a) $RbCl < KCl < NaCl$;   (1)
    (b) $NaCl < KCl < RbCl$;   (1)
    (c) the values differ from the expected order since polarisability
    arguments ignore other important factors such as lattice energy.   (1)

The maximum possible score for this test is 15.

Chapter 7: Bond Types in Simple Inorganic Compounds

1. $(x_A - x_B)$ is large, i.e. more than about 1.5.   (1), (1)

2. Covalent if x_A, x_B are both large; metallic if x_A, x_B are both small.   (1), (1)

3. Less covalent (more ionic).   (1)

4. More covalent (less ionic).   (1)

5. (a) Ionic;   (b) chiefly covalent;   (c) mainly covalent;
    (d) metallic;   (e) covalent.   (1), (1), (1), (1), (1)

6. None, to a first approximation.   (1)

7. More covalent in passing from RbF to MoF_6.   (1)

8. (a) Mainly covalent;   (b) chiefly ionic;   (c) metallic;
    (d) covalent.   (1), (1), (1), (1)

9. (a), (c) and (d).   (1), (1), (1)

The maximum possible score for this test is 20.

Index

Figures in italics are pages where the data is tabulated.